Favourite Christmas Stories from

Fireside Al

SELECTED
AND
INTRODUCED
BY

ALAN MAITLAND

VIKING

VIKING
Published by the Penguin Group
Penguin Books Canada Ltd, 10 Alcorn Avenue, Toronto, Ontario M4V 3B2
Penguin Books Ltd, 27 Wrights Lane, London W8 5TZ, England
Viking Penguin, a division of Penguin Books USA Inc., 375 Hudson Street,
New York, New York 10014, U.S.A.
Penguin Books Australia Ltd, Ringwood, Victoria, Australia
Penguin Books (NZ) Ltd, 182–190 Wairau Road, Auckland 10, New Zealand

Penguin Books Ltd, Registered Offices: Harmondsworth, Middlesex, England

First published 1995
10 9 8 7 6 5 4 3 2

Introductions, Notes and Selection Copyright © Alan Maitland, 1995

Printed and bound in Canada on acid-free paper ⊛

Canadian Cataloguing in Publication Data

Main entry under title:

Favourite Christmas stories from Fireside Al

ISBN 0-670-86537-0

1. Christmas stories, English. 2. Christmas stories, Canadian (English).*
3. Christmas stories, American. 4. English fiction - 19th century. 5. English
fiction - 20th century. 6. Canadian fiction (English) - 20th century.*
7. American fiction - 19th century. 8. American fiction - 20th century.
I. Maitland, Alan.

PR1309.C5F38 1995   823'.010833   C95-930781-8

Copyright acknowledgments appear on page 295.

This book is dedicated to our dearly lamented friend
Bunny (McLeod) and to our dog Gretzky,
who pinned Bunny in her mink coat to the dishwasher
for an hour because she didn't come to church
on Christmas Eve.

As we grow older, let us be more thankful that
the circle of our Christmas associations
and of the lessons that they bring, expands!
Let us welcome every one of them,
and summon them to take their places
by the Christmas hearth.

Charles Dickens

ACKNOWLEDGMENTS

I am indebted to CBC's Mark Starowicz for starting the stories on "As It Happens," and of course to those who continued them. To Barbara Frum who dubbed me Fireside Al. To Jackie Kaiser of Penguin for transferring them from tape to the written page. It's exciting to see them collected in print. To George Jamieson and Don Mason for doing much of the early work, and to Don for his help on historical matters. And to the many who have enjoyed the stories over the years on CBC radio. Now you can read them for yourselves. Enjoy!

Fireside Al

INTRODUCTION

The old clock by the corner-hearth is mumbling something about midnight, and "won't you *ever* go to bed?" But the fire is low, and the house is quietly sleeping as the glowing embers slowly rekindle in their grate, adding a gentle, slumbering warmth to the passing hours of night. Quietly I hear the stories of Christmases long ago conversing with those of the more pressing present.

A Christmas story-bag is a sack made of canvas to hold the magic whispers: in go the stories, year after year. You shake them about, give them a stir, allow them to ferment. You carry their growing bulk on your back from childhood through the years. Some become cumbersome, or weary of the road—these you sort through, and gently put aside. Others take on a deeper resonance over time, as if the journey is somehow made fruitful by their company. These you once more wrap warmly in their covers, with a wonder made fuller with the years. And then, a final sorting through, and out come the stories once more: some now wrapped in gold, others in silver, some in the finest tissue.

This is a collection I take particular pleasure in. I like to think that I enjoy all the seasons equally, but Christmas holds its special place, and the stories here reflect that special pleasure. Two lost stories by Victorian women writers—Elizabeth Wetherell and Amy Lothrop's "The Story of the Christmas Stocking," and

E. Lynn Linton's "The Old Lady's Story"—have remained unreprinted since their original publication in the 1850s. It is a pleasure to include them here. Also, Laurence Housman's "The Lovely Messengers," first published in the 1890s and quite forgotten, holds a particularly persuasive charm. And then there's "The Shepherd," a story that takes me every Christmas Eve on a cold, dark, eerie flight across the North Sea.

And the list goes on and on. "Paddington's Christmas" and Maxim Gorky's "Christmas Phantoms." A little poem by Patrick Brontë, the father of Emily, Anne and Charlotte. "The True Meaning of Crumbfest," a delightful new story about Christmas mice on Prince Edward Island. And Dickens, of course, and Margaret Atwood, W.O. Mitchell and Oscar Wilde. Nikos Kazantzakis's wonderful "In Calabria." Too many stories that bear a special mention. So I will simply say a "Merry Christmas" and wish you all the best of reading. And, finally, as I think has been said before, "God Bless Us, Every One!"

TABLE OF CONTENTS

Favourite Christmas Stories from

Fireside Al

Christmas at Fezziwig's Warehouse

by
CHARLES DICKENS
(1812–1870)

A little dance with Dickens. A toast from old Fezziwig to start the Christmas season. The irrepressible, broad-beamed Fezziwig following a "corkscrew" with a "cut"—his skinny calves winking and shining out like little moons, dancing to a fiddled tune across the warehouse floor.

"**Y**o ho, my boys!" said Fezziwig. "No more work to-night. Christmas Eve, Dick. Christmas, Ebenezer! Let's have the shutters up," cried old Fezziwig, with a sharp clap of his hands, "before a man can say, Jack Robinson!"

…"Hilly-ho!" cried old Fezziwig, skipping down from the high desk, with wonderful agility. "Clear away, my lads, and let's have lots of room here! Hilli-ho, Dick! Chirrup, Ebenezer!"

Clear away! There was nothing they wouldn't have cleared away, or couldn't have cleared away, with old Fezziwig looking on. It was done in a minute. Every movable was packed off, as if it were dismissed from public life for evermore; the floor was swept and watered, the lamps were trimmed, fuel was heaped upon the fire; and the warehouse was as snug, and warm, and dry, and bright a ball-room, as you would desire to see upon a winter's night.

In came a fiddler with a music-book, and went up to the lofty desk, and made an orchestra of it, and tuned like fifty stomach-aches. In came Mrs. Fezziwig, one vast substantial smile. In came the three Miss Fezziwigs, beaming and loveable. In came the six young followers whose hearts they broke. In came all the young men and women employed in the business. In came the housemaid, with her cousin, the baker. In came the cook, with her brother's particular friend, the milkman. In came the boy from over the way, who was suspected of not having board enough from his master; trying to hide himself behind the girl from next door but one, who was proved to have had her ears pulled by her Mistress. In they all came, one after another; some shyly, some boldly, some gracefully, some awkwardly, some pushing, some pulling; in they all came, anyhow and everyhow. Away they all went, twenty couples at once, hands half round and back again the other way; down the middle and up again; round and round in various stages of affectionate grouping; old top couple always turning up in the wrong place; new top couple starting off again, as soon as they got there; all top couples at last, and not a bottom one to help them. When this result was brought about, old Fezziwig, clapping his hands to stop the dance, cried out, "Well done!" and the fiddler plunged his hot face into a pot of porter, especially provided for that purpose. But scorning rest upon his reappearance, he instantly began again, though there were no dancers yet, as if the other fiddler had been carried home, exhausted, on a shutter; and he were a bran-new man resolved to beat him out of sight, or perish.

There were more dances, and there were forfeits, and more dances, and there was cake, and there was negus, and there was a great piece of Cold Roast, and there was a great piece of Cold Boiled, and there were mince-pies, and plenty of beer. But the great effect of the evening came after the Roast and Boiled, when the fiddler (an artful dog, mind! The sort of man who knew his business better than you or I could have told it him!) struck up "Sir Roger de Coverley." Then old Fezziwig stood out to dance with Mrs. Fezziwig. Top couple too; with a good stiff piece of work cut out for them; three or four and twenty pair of partners; people who were not to be trifled with; people who *would* dance, and had no notion of walking.

But if they had been twice as many: ah, four times: old Fezziwig would have been a match for them, and so would Mrs. Fezziwig. As to *her*, she was worthy to be his partner in every sense of the term. If that's not high praise, tell me higher, and I'll use it. A positive light appeared to issue from Fezziwig's calves. They shone in every part of the dance like moons. You couldn't have predicted, at any given time, what would become of 'em next. And when old Fezziwig and Mrs. Fezziwig had gone all through the dance; advance and retire, hold hands with your partner; bow and curtsey; corkscrew; thread-the-needle, and back again to your place; Fezziwig "cut"—cut so deftly, that he appeared to wink with his legs, and came upon his feet again without a stagger.

When the clock struck eleven, this domestic ball broke up. Mr. and Mrs. Fezziwig took their stations, one on either side the door, and shaking hands with every person individually as he or she went out, wished him or her a Merry Christmas.

Paddington's Christmas

by
MICHAEL BOND
(1926–   )

Paddington is my very favourite little bear. He plays his Christmas part with the skill of a seasoned performer: how closely he times his entrances, his exits; how skillfully he delivers his lines. For Paddington is no ordinary little bear—and his Christmas is a Christmas of extraordinary proportions.

Paddington found that Christmas took a long time to come. Each morning when he hurried downstairs he crossed the date off the calendar, but the more days he crossed off the farther away it seemed.

However, there was plenty to occupy his mind. For one thing, the postman started arriving later and later in the morning, and when he did finally reach the Browns' house there were so many letters to deliver he had a job to push them all through the letter-box. Often there were mysterious-looking parcels as well, which Mrs Bird promptly hid before Paddington had time to squeeze them.

A surprising number of the envelopes were addressed to Paddington himself, and he carefully made a list of all those who had sent him Christmas cards so that he could be sure of thanking them.

"You may be only a small bear," said Mrs Bird, as she helped him arrange the cards on the mantelpiece, "but you certainly leave your mark."

Paddington wasn't sure how to take this, especially as Mrs Bird had just polished the hall floor, but when he examined his paws they were quite clean.

Paddington had made his own Christmas cards. Some he had drawn himself, decorating the edges with holly and mistletoe; others had been made out of pictures cut from Mrs Brown's magazines. But each one had the words A MERRY CHRISTMAS AND A HAPPY NEW YEAR printed on the front, and they were signed PADINGTUN BROWN on the inside—together with his special paw mark to show that they were genuine.

Paddington wasn't sure about the spelling of A MERRY CHRISTMAS. It didn't look at all right. But Mrs Bird checked all the words in a dictionary for him to make certain.

"I don't suppose many people get Christmas cards from a bear," she explained. "They'll probably want to keep them, so you ought to make sure they are right."

One evening Mr Brown arrived home with a huge Christmas tree tied to the roof of his car. It was placed in a position of hon-our by the dining-room window and both Paddington and Mr Brown spent a long time decorating it with coloured electric lights and silver tinsel.

Apart from the Christmas tree, there were paper chains and holly to be put up, and large coloured bells made of crinkly paper. Paddington enjoyed doing the paper chains. He managed to persuade Mr Brown that bears were very good at putting up decorations and together they did most of the house, with Paddington standing on Mr Brown's shoulders while Mr Brown handed up the drawing pins. It came to an unhappy end one evening when Paddington accidentally put his paw on a draw-ing pin which he'd left on top of Mr Brown's head. When Mrs Bird rushed into the dining-room to see what all the fuss was about, and to inquire why all the lights had suddenly gone out, she found Paddington hanging by his paws from the chandelier and Mr Brown dancing round the room rubbing his head.

But by then the decorations were almost finished and the house had taken on quite a festive air. The sideboard was groan-ing under the weight of nuts and oranges, dates and figs, none of which Paddington was allowed to touch, and Mr Brown had stopped smoking his pipe and was filling the air instead with the smell of cigars.

The excitement in the Browns' house mounted, until it reached fever pitch a few days before Christmas, when Jonathan and Judy arrived home for the holidays.

But if the days leading up to Christmas were busy and excit-ing, they were nothing compared with Christmas Day itself.

The Browns were up early on Christmas morning—much earlier than they had intended. It all started when Paddington woke to find a large pillow case at the bottom of his bed. His eyes nearly popped out with astonishment when he switched his torch on, for it was bulging with parcels, and it certainly hadn't been there when he'd gone to bed on Christmas Eve.

Paddington's eyes grew larger and larger as he unwrapped the brightly coloured paper round each present. A few days before, on Mrs Bird's instructions, he had made a list of all the things he hoped to have given him and had hidden it up one of the chimneys. It was a strange thing, but everything on that list seemed to be in the pillow case.

There was a large chemistry outfit from Mr Brown, full of jars and bottles and test tubes, which looked very interesting. And there was a miniature xylophone from Mrs Brown, which pleased him no end. Paddington was fond of music—especially the loud sort, which was good for conducting—and he had always wanted something he could actually play.

Mrs Bird's parcel was even more exciting, for it contained a checked cap which he'd especially asked for and had underlined on his list. Paddington stood on the end of his bed, admiring the effect in the mirror for quite a while.

Jonathan and Judy had each given him a travel book. Paddington was very interested in geography, being a much-travelled bear, and he was pleased to see there were plenty of maps and coloured pictures inside.

The noise from Paddington's room was soon sufficient to waken both Jonathan and Judy, and in no time at all the whole house was in an uproar, with wrapping paper and bits of string everywhere.

"I'm as patriotic as the next man," grumbled Mr Brown. "But I draw the line when bears start playing the National Anthem at six o'clock in the morning—especially on a xylophone."

As always, it was left to Mrs Bird to restore order. "No more presents until after lunch," she said, firmly. She had just tripped over Paddington on the upstairs landing, where he was investigating his new chemical outfit, and something nasty had gone in one of her slippers.

"It's all right, Mrs Bird," said Paddington, consulting his

instruction book, "it's only some iron filings. I don't think they're dangerous."

"Dangerous or not," said Mrs Bird, "I've a big dinner to cook—not to mention your birthday cake to finish decorating."

Being a bear, Paddington had two birthdays each year—one in the summer and one at Christmas—and the Browns were holding a party in his honour to which Mr Gruber had been invited.

After they'd had breakfast and been to church, the morning passed quickly and Paddington spent most of his time trying to decide what to do next. With so many things from which to choose it was most difficult. He read some chapters from his books and made several interesting smells and a small explosion with his chemical outfit.

Mr Brown was already in trouble for having given it to him, especially when Paddington found a chapter in the instruction book headed "Indoor Fireworks." He made himself a "never ending" snake which wouldn't stop growing and frightened Mrs Bird to death when she met it coming down the stairs.

"If we don't watch out," she confided to Mrs Brown, "we shan't last over Christmas. We shall either be blown to smithereens or poisoned. He was testing my gravy with some litmus paper just now."

Mrs Brown sighed. "It's a good job Christmas only comes once a year," she said, as she helped Mrs Bird with the potatoes.

"It isn't over yet," warned Mrs Bird.

Fortunately, Mr Gruber arrived at that moment and some measure of order was established before they all sat down to dinner.

Paddington's eyes glistened as he surveyed the table. He didn't agree with Mr Brown when he said it all looked too good to eat. All the same, even Paddington got noticeably slower towards the end when Mrs Bird brought in the Christmas pudding.

"Well," said Mr Gruber, a few minutes later, as he sat back and surveyed his empty plate, "I must say that's the best Christmas dinner I've had for many a day. Thank you very much indeed!"

"Hear! Hear!" agreed Mr Brown. "What do you say,

Paddington?"

"It was very nice," said Paddington, licking some cream from his whiskers. "Except I had a bone in my Christmas pudding."

"You *what*?" exclaimed Mrs Brown. "Don't be silly—there are no bones in Christmas pudding."

"I had one," said Paddington, firmly. "It was all hard—and it stuck in my throat."

"Good gracious!" exclaimed Mrs Bird. "The sixpence! I always put a piece of silver in the Christmas pudding."

"What!" said Paddington, nearly falling off his chair. "A sixpence? I've never heard of a sixpence pudding before."

"Quick," shouted Mr Brown, rising to the emergency. "Turn him upside down."

Before Paddington could reply, he found himself hanging head downwards while Mr Brown and Mr Gruber took it in turns to shake him. The rest of the family stood round watching the floor.

"It's no good," said Mr Brown, after a while. "It must have gone too far." He helped Mr Gruber lift Paddington into an armchair where he lay gasping for breath.

"I've got a magnet upstairs," said Jonathan. "We could try lowering it down his throat on a piece of string."

"I don't think so, dear," said Mrs Brown, in a worried tone of voice. "He might swallow that and then we should be even worse off." She bent over the chair. "How do you feel, Paddington?"

"Sick," said Paddington, in an aggrieved tone of voice.

"Of course you do, dear," said Mrs Brown. "It's only to be expected. There's only one thing to do—we shall have to send for the doctor."

"Thank goodness I scrubbed it first," said Mrs Bird. "It might have been covered with germs."

"But I *didn't* swallow it," gasped Paddington. "I only nearly did. Then I put it on the side of my plate. I didn't know it was a sixpence because it was all covered with Christmas pudding."

Paddington felt very fed up. He'd just eaten one of the best dinners he could ever remember and now he'd been turned upside down and shaken without even being given time to explain.

Everyone exchanged glances and then crept quietly away, leaving Paddington to recover by himself. There didn't seem to be much they *could* say.

But after the dinner things had been cleared away, and by the time Mrs Bird had made some strong coffee, Paddington was almost himself again. He was sitting up in the chair helping himself to some dates when they trooped back into the room. It took a lot to make Paddington ill for very long.

When they had finished their coffee, and were sitting round the blazing fire feeling warm and comfortable, Mr Brown rubbed his hands. "Now, Paddington," he said, "it's not only Christmas, it's your birthday as well. What would you like to do?"

A mysterious expression came over Paddington's face. "If you all go in the other room," he announced, "I've a special surprise for you."

"Oh dear, *must* we, Paddington?" said Mrs Brown. "There isn't a fire."

"I shan't be long," said Paddington, firmly. "But it's a special surprise and it has to be prepared." He held the door open and the Browns, Mrs Bird and Mr Gruber filed obediently into the other room.

"Now close your eyes," said Paddington, when they were all settled, "and I'll let you know when I'm ready."

Mrs Brown shivered. "I hope you won't be too long," she called. But the only reply was the sound of the door clicking shut.

They waited for several minutes without speaking, and then Mr Gruber cleared his throat. "Do you think young Mr Brown's forgotten about us?" he asked.

"I don't know," said Mrs Brown. "But I'm not waiting much longer."

"Henry!" she exclaimed, as she opened her eyes. "Have you gone to sleep?"

"Er, wassat?" snorted Mr Brown. He had eaten such a large dinner he was finding it difficult to keep awake. "What's happening? Have I missed anything?"

"Nothing's happening," said Mrs Brown. "Henry, you'd better go and see what Paddington's up to."

Several more minutes went by before Mr Brown returned to announce that he couldn't find Paddington anywhere.

"Well, he must be *somewhere*," said Mrs Brown. "Bears don't disappear into thin air."

"Crikey!" exclaimed Jonathan, as a thought suddenly struck him. "You don't think he's playing at Father Christmas, do you? He was asking all about it the other day when he put his list up the chimney. I bet that's why he wanted us to come in here— because this chimney connects with the one upstairs—and there isn't a fire."

"Father Christmas?" said Mr Brown. "I'll give him Father Christmas!" He stuck his head up the chimney and called Paddington's name several times. "I can't see anything," he said, striking a match. As if in answer a large lump of soot descended and burst on top of his head.

"Now look what you've done, Henry," said Mrs Brown. "Shouting so—you've disturbed the soot. All over your clean shirt!"

"If it *is* young Mr Brown, perhaps he's stuck somewhere," suggested Mr Gruber. "He did have rather a large dinner. I remember wondering at the time where he put it all."

Mr Gruber's suggestion had an immediate effect on the party and everyone began to look serious.

"Why, he might suffocate with the fumes," exclaimed Mrs Bird, as she hurried outside to the broom cupboard.

When she returned, armed with a mop, everyone took it in turns to poke it up the chimney but even though they strained their ears they couldn't hear a sound.

It was while this excitement was at its height that Paddington came into the room. He looked most surprised when he saw Mr Brown with his head up the chimney.

"You can come into the dining-room now," he announced, looking round the room. "I've finished wrapping my presents and they're all on the Christmas tree."

"You don't mean to say," spluttered Mr Brown, as he sat in the fireplace rubbing his face with a handkerchief, "you've been in the other room all the time?"

"Yes," said Paddington, innocently. "I hope I didn't keep you waiting too long."

Mrs Brown looked at her husband. "I thought you said you'd looked everywhere," she exclaimed.

"Well—we'd just come from the dining-room," said Mr Brown, looking very sheepish. "I didn't think he'd be *there*."

"It only goes to show," said Mrs Bird hastily, as she caught sight of the expression on Mr Brown's face, "how easy it is to give a bear a bad name."

Paddington looked most interested when they explained to him what all the fuss was about.

"I never thought of coming down the chimney," he said, staring at the fireplace.

"Well, you're not thinking about it now either," replied Mr Brown, sternly.

But even Mr Brown's expression changed as he followed Paddington into the dining-room and saw the surprise that had been prepared for them.

In addition to the presents that had already been placed on the tree, there were now six newly wrapped ones tied to the lower branches. If the Browns recognized the wrapping paper they had used for Paddington's presents earlier in the day, they were much too polite to say anything.

"I'm afraid I had to use old paper," said Paddington apologetically, as he waved a paw at the tree. "I hadn't any money left. That's why you had to go in the other room while I wrapped them."

"Really, Paddington," said Mrs Brown. "I'm very cross with you—spending all your money on presents for us."

"I'm afraid they're rather ordinary," said Paddington, as he settled back in a chair to watch the others. "But I hope you like them. They're all labelled so that you know which is which."

"Ordinary?" exclaimed Mr Brown, as he opened his parcel. "I don't call a pipe rack ordinary. And there's an ounce of my favourite tobacco tied to the back as well!"

"Gosh! A new stamp album!" cried Jonathan. "Whizzo! And it's got some stamps inside already."

"They're Peruvian ones from Aunt Lucy's postcards," said Paddington. "I've been saving them for you."

"And I've got a box of paints," exclaimed Judy. "Thank you very much, Paddington. It's just what I wanted."

"We all seem to be lucky," said Mrs Brown, as she unwrapped a parcel containing a bottle of her favourite lavender water. "How *did* you guess? I finished my last bottle only a week ago."

"I'm sorry about your parcel, Mrs Bird," said Paddington, looking across the room. "I had a bit of a job with the knots."

"It must be something special," said Mr Brown. "It seems all string and no parcel."

"That's because it's really clothes line," explained Paddington, "not string. I rescued it when I got stuck in the revolving door at Crumbold and Ferns."

"That makes two presents in one," said Mrs Bird, as she freed the last of the knots and began unwinding yards and yards of paper. "How exciting. I can't think what it can be."

"Why," she exclaimed. "I do believe it's a brooch! And it's shaped like a bear—how lovely!" Mrs Bird looked most touched as she handed the present round for everyone to see. "I shall keep it in a safe place," she added, "and only wear it on special occasions—when I want to impress people."

"I don't know what mine is," said Mr Gruber, as they all turned to him. He squeezed the parcel. "It's such a funny shape."

"It's a drinking mug!" he exclaimed, his face lighting up with pleasure. "And it even has my name painted on the side!"

"It's for your elevenses, Mr Gruber," said Paddington. "I noticed your old one was getting rather chipped."

"I'm sure it will make my cocoa taste better than it ever has before," said Mr Gruber.

He stood up and cleared his throat. "I think I would like to offer a vote of thanks to young Mr Brown," he said, "for all his nice presents. I'm sure he must have given them a great deal of thought."

"Hear! Hear!" echoed Mr Brown, as he filled his pipe.

Mr Gruber felt under his chair. "And while I think of it, Mr Brown, I have a small present for you."

Everyone stood round and watched while Paddington struggled with his parcel, eager to see what Mr Gruber had bought him. A gasp of surprise went up as he tore the paper to one side, for it was a beautifully bound leather scrapbook, with "Paddington Brown" printed in gold leaf on the cover.

Paddington didn't know what to say, but Mr Gruber waved

his thanks to one side. "I know how you enjoy writing about your adventures, Mr Brown," he said. "And you have so many I'm sure your present scrapbook must be almost full."

"It is," said Paddington, earnestly. "And I'm sure I shall have lots more. Things happen to me, you know. But I shall only put my best ones in here!"

When he made his way up to bed later that evening, his mind was in such a whirl, and he was so full of good things, he could hardly climb the stairs—let alone think about anything. He wasn't quite sure which he had enjoyed the most. The presents, the Christmas dinner, the games, or the tea—with the special marmalade-layer birthday cake Mrs Bird had made in his honour. Pausing on the corner half-way up, he decided he had enjoyed giving his own presents best of all.

"Paddington! Whatever have you got there?" He jumped and hastily hid his paw behind his back as he heard Mrs Bird calling from the bottom of the stairs.

"It's only some sixpence pudding, Mrs Bird," he called, looking over the banisters guiltily. "I thought I might get hungry during the night and I didn't want to take any chances."

"Honestly!" Mrs Bird exclaimed, as she was joined by the others. "What *does* that bear look like? A paper hat about ten sizes too big on his head—Mr Gruber's scrapbook in one paw—and a plate of Christmas pudding in the other!"

"I don't care what he looks like," said Mrs Brown, "so long as he stays that way. The place wouldn't be the same without him."

But Paddington was too far away to hear what was being said. He was already sitting up in bed, busily writing in his scrapbook.

First of all, there was a very important notice to go on the front page. It said:

PADINGTUN BROWN,
32 WINDSOR GARDENS,
LUNDUN,
ENGLAND,
YUROPE,
THE WORLD.

Then, on the next page he added, in large capital letters: MY ADDVENTURES. CHAPTER WUN.

Paddington sucked his pen thoughtfully for a moment and then carefully replaced the top on the bottle of ink before it had a chance to fall over on the sheets. He felt much too sleepy to write any more. But he didn't really mind. Tomorrow was another day—and he felt quite sure he *would* have some more adventures—even if he didn't know what they were going to be as yet.

Paddington lay back and pulled the blankets up round his whiskers. It was warm and comfortable and he sighed contentedly as he closed his eyes. It was nice being a bear. Especially a bear called Paddington.

The
Santa Claus Trap

by
MARGARET ATWOOD
(1939–   )

In terms of sheer nastiness, meanness and petty hatred, Margaret Atwood's Mr. Grate makes Scrooge look, well, less Scroogely. Taking his lemonade without any sugar, because he likes it sour, Mr. Grate is one of the many memorable additions to the Atwood gallery of villainous creations. As Charlotte, the little girl in "The Santa Claus Trap," relates, "Some people are naughty, but Mr. Grate is bad."

nce upon a time there was a man named Mr. Grate,
Whom the thought of Christmas filled
With an indescribable and fungoid hate.

He hated Christmas trees and presents
And carols and turkeys and plum
Puddings, and he thought Santa Claus and his reindeer
Were not only dumb

But ought to be banned and not allowed
Into the country,
And dogs that barked and children who laughed
Too much made him furious,
And he wished they would all fall down
Holes or drown in bogs.

Mr. Grate, although he was quite rich,
Lived in one miserable little room
Which he never cleaned with a vacuum cleaner
Or swept with a broom
So that it was all covered with dust and dirt
And spiderwebs and old pieces of cheese
And so was Mr. Grate,

And if you ever came near him
You would begin to cough and sneeze,

But nobody ever did, because he never went outside,
But stayed in,
And counted his money, and wrote nasty letters to the editor,
And sometimes drank a bottle of gin

All by himself, or a glass of lemonade without any sugar,
Because he liked it sour,
And he peered out the window
   and hated everybody,
By the hour.

He had round eyes like an owl's
And his face was all squizzled up
And covered with frowns and
   scowls.

One day in December, Mr. Grate
   thought up a horrible plot.
"Everyone," he said to himself—he
   talked out loud a lot—
"Has a lot of nice things, much nicer
   than anything *I've* got,

And every Christmas they give each other presents,
And nobody ever gives *me* none,
And not only that, but I never have any fun,

And Santa Claus comes and fills their stockings
And panti-hose and socklets
With oranges and licorice sticks and bubble gum
And chocolates.

But what if Santa Claus were to suddenly disappear,
And all that ever gets found is his empty sled and reindeer?
What if I could kidnap Santa Claus and keep him in a sack
And say I would never give him back

Unless the children sent ME all their candy
And jellybeans and maybe a teddy bear?
Not only would I get even with them and give them a scare,
But I'd have all the stuff, and maybe I'd even be a millionaire.

I'll keep Santa Claus in a cupboard
And feed him on water and crumbs,
While I sit outside and laugh myself silly
And stuff myself with candy apples and bubble gums!"

And for the first time in a long long while,
Mr. Grate began to laugh and chuckle,
But it wasn't a nice laugh, and he turned all red and purple
And rolled around on the floor
And had to loosen his belt buckle.

After that he got up again and set to work.
"The thing is," he said to himself,
"Santa Claus is obviously a jerk

All he ever does is give things to people—
It's really shocking—
And he can't seem to resist an unfilled stocking.

Therefore, all I have to do is get a lot of stockings,
And hang them all over the room as a kind of bait,
And build a trap in the fireplace which will catch him
When he comes down the chimney,
And then I'll just sit and wait."

So first Mr. Grate went to a Sale,
And bought a whole armful of stockings
And socks and mukluks and several rubber boots,
Pushing old ladies out of his way
And scowling and frowning at the men
Who were ringing bells, dressed up in Santa Claus suits,

And then he went to a junk yard and bought all kinds of junk:
Some pieces of old cars, a wringer washing machine,

Several rolls of barbed wire,
Some string and rubber bands, a wrench, a lever, a gear,
And a box full of old tin cans
Which unfortunately also contained a dead skunk,

But that's life, said Mr. Grate to himself
As he carted all these things home
In a U-Haul he'd rented.
And when he got them back to his room, he started to build
The most complicated trap that has ever been invented.

The trap was foolproof and full of pulleys and levers,
And anyone who came down the chimney and stepped into it
Would be grabbed by mechanical hands
And rollered on rollers and tangled in wires and zoomed
Right into a sack in Mr. Grate's closet,
And it looked as if Santa Claus was doomed,

EXCEPT

Next door to Mr. Grate lived some twins,
A girl named Charlotte and a boy named William.
Charlotte's favorite flower was the Rose,
And William's was the Trillium.

They were both very curious
And they were always looking in people's windows
And back yards and bureau drawers or over their shoulders.
Charlotte was somewhat self-contained,
But William was bolder.

And one day, when Mr. Grate was building his trap and
Talking out loud to himself
About his plan to hold Santa Claus to ransom,
Charlotte just happened to be standing on William's shoulders
And looking through his transom.

She overheard the whole plan, and she was so dismayed
She almost fell off,

And then she almost gave them away,
Because even Mr. Grate's transom was so dusty
It made her cough,

But luckily Mr. Grate was hammering something
At the time, and didn't hear.
Charlotte climbed down and whispered in William's ear,
"William, I have just heard the most terrible thing,
And Christmas is going to be ruined this year!"
These words of Charlotte's filled William's heart with fear.

The twins hurried back to their own house,
And sat down at the kitchen table,
And while they were eating some peanut butter sandwiches
To keep up their strength,
Charlotte repeated what she had heard, and well as she was
        able.

"But that's terrible!" said William. "If Santa Claus is caught
In the trap, and tied up with a large knot,

No children in the entire world
Will get anything in their stockings, you see!
And—I hardly need to point out—
That includes you and me.
I feel that this could turn into a major catastrophe."

"Don't be so obvious," Charlotte said.
"The main thing is, how can we stop him?"
"Well," said William,
"I could go over there with my baseball bat and bop him
On the head." "You aren't big enough,"
Charlotte said, she was practical.
"We have to think of a plan that is both feasible and tactical,

By which I mean something we can do ourselves
That will actually work."
But the possibility of no Santa Claus
Filled them with depression, gloom, and murk.

And they found it hard to even think about it,
It made them so sad.
"Some people are naughty," said Charlotte,
"But Mr. Grate is *bad*."

For days they did nothing but sigh and mutter
And eat sandwiches made of peanut butter.

Once they went to spy on Mr. Grate,
But the trap was even bigger,
And Mr. Grate was rubbing his hands
And looking at it, with a nasty snigger.

The sight of the enormous trap
Made Charlotte and William feel helpless and small,
And they seemed unable to think of anything to do at all.

They knew they couldn't tell the police or any grownups,
Because no one would believe them anyway,
And it was too late to write Santa Claus to warn him,
Because Christmas was due now any day.

"Is this the end?" said William, feeling doleful.
"Do not give up," said Charlotte, looking soulful.

AT LAST

They had a brilliant idea, and being twins
They had it both at once, because
Twins often do. "I know!" they cried together.
"We'll make a false Santa Claus!

We'll make it out of red potato sacks, and fill it full of rocks,
And let it down Mr. Grate's chimney on a rope,
And it will snarl up the trap and possibly break it, because
Of the rocks." This idea filled them with hope.
"Come on," said William, "let's get going,
We have no time to waste!"
So, pausing only to eat one more small sandwich each
And to put on their winter coats
And their mittens, boots and hats,
They rushed out the door in considerable haste.

"Where are they going?"
Their mother called after them as they ran down the street.
"We're going to save Santa Claus!" they called back, and
Not realizing the seriousness of the situation,
She said, "Isn't that sweet."

It was Christmas Eve, and Mr. Grate
Had hung up his stocking, or I should say
His stockings, because he had about a hundred of them
Dangling all over his room,
In every color you can think of,
Red, green, yellow, purple, blue, and gray,
And the total effect would have been rather joyous and gay

If it hadn't been for the sinister machine
Lurking near the fireplace in the corner.
"All right, Santa Claus," muttered Mr. Grate,
"Once down that chimney and you're a goner!"

He was sitting in his one dingy old chair,
Hugging himself and chortling,
When up on his roof he heard an odd sound,
Part scuffling and part snortling.

"It must be a reindeer!" cried Mr. Grate, and jumped up
To give the final touch to his arrangement of socks.
(It was actually Charlotte and William,
Having a little trouble with the rocks.)

"Now Santa will slide down the chimney
With a nice, round, fat kind of slither,
And I'll have him safe in my closet,
And all the children of the world will be thrown into a dither,

And serve them right," said Mr. Grate.
He could hardly wait.

But imagine his surprise
When instead of a round little man landing
With a comfortable plop in his trap, there was a loud crash!
Followed by a thud and a rattle and a smash!

Someone—or something—dressed in red
Had come down the chimney, though it wasn't light
Enough to see clearly, and Mr. Grate's trap had spun into action,
But it was throwing out sparks left and right!

Its mechanical arms were getting all snarled up
In the barbed wire,
And its washing machine wringer was out of control,
Spinning higher and higher,
And something seemed to be wrong
With the sack that Santa was supposed to fall into—
It had caught on fire!

Suddenly all the fuses blew,
And a thin, tiny, eerie voice came wafting
Down the chimney flue:

"Mr. Grate! Mr. Grate!

REPENT

Before it is too late!"

This was actually Charlotte,
Which Mr. Grate had no way of knowing.
"It's ghosts!" he cried.
"I've got to get out of here, even though it's snowing!"

He ran towards the door, but because
There were now no lights in the entire place,
He tripped over something and fell flat on his face.

Then something else grabbed him from behind,
And one of the gears that wasn't broken began to grind,

And then there was an unpleasant ZAP
And Mr. Grate was caught in his own trap!

"Help, Help," he cried, and began to struggle,
Which only made the tangle worse,
"I'm perishing! I'm expiring!
I need a doctor and also a nurse! O curse

The day I decided to trap poor Santa Claus!
Please, someone, bring some wire clippers and tinsnips,
And wrenches, and saws
And get me out!"

Charlotte and William, on the roof, heard his feeble shout.
"I believe it's worked," Charlotte said. "He seems to be caught,
Which is more than we expected.
Should we let him out, or not?"

Mr. Grate was lying all covered with barbed wire
And bits of cheese from the floor,
And feeling decidedly sorry for himself,
And also rather battered and sore,
When Charlotte and William climbed
Through the transom over his door.

(They didn't have a key, and the door itself was locked.)
"Well," said Charlotte, looking down at Mr. Grate,
Where he lay clinking and clanking,
"In my opinion you deserve a good spanking."

"In *my* opinion," said William,
"You deserve a good kick in the behind."
"But," said Charlotte, intervening—
She felt one should be polite, if at all possible—
"This is Christmas and we are going to be kind.

We'll get you out of the trap *this* time,
If you promise not to do it again, and make amends."
"But why did you think of such an evil thing to do
In the first place?" said William.
"Boohoo," said Mr. Grate, "I don't have any friends,

Or a teddy bear, or *anything*,
And everyone else was having such a good time,
Especially at Christmas, and my room is all covered with grime,
And no one invites me to dinner,
And I never get anything in my stocking but pieces of coal,
Or sometimes a hole,
Or a rotten potato, and once, in a good year, a single Smartie,
And it's a long long time since I even went to a birthday party!"

"There, there," said Charlotte, wiping away his grubby tears,
While William was snipping him out of the trap
With a pair of shears,

"I understand perfectly. You just wanted some attention."
(Which had been said to her on several occasions
When she herself has been rather surly,
But these we won't mention.)

"You can come back to *our* house for Christmas.
I'm sure our Mum won't mind, if we ask,
And we'll even help you clean up your room."
Which they did, and it was an unpleasant task…

But in Mr. Grate's closet they found a couple of suits
That weren't too dirty,
And when they had washed his face and shined his boots

He looked quite presentable,
And was so pleased he actually smiled
And allowed his fingernails to be cut and his moustache filed,
And off they all went to Charlotte's and William's house,
And had a wonderful Christmas dinner
With lots of trimmings,
And when Mr. Grate got up from the table
He was certainly not thinner.

And after that day, though he was not
A completely different person, and still
Didn't like dogs much, and was known to spill

A few bits of cheese on the carpet now and then,
He was much nicer than before,
And played Monopoly with Charlotte and William,
So that they were quite glad he lived next door.

And he changed the spelling of his name to Mr. Great,
And often said things like "It's never too late."

"And although he didn't manage
To *catch* Santa Claus," said Charlotte one day,
"At least he *found* him."
Which is true, when you think about it, in a way,

And also he had found not only one friend
But two. Which is a pretty good place to say

THE END.

Christmas Phantoms

Attributed to
MAXIM GORKY
(1868–1936)

The script of the "Christmas Phantoms" has lain in the CBC vaults for decades. The difficulties began when we attempted to trace the story to include it in this collection. After consulting a number of people from various Russian Studies departments across the country, and after sifting through as much of Gorky's work as we could possibly lay our hands on, we were still unable to make a positive trace on this story. So the text that follows is from the original CBC script, and we have attributed it to Gorky. It's simply too good to overlook.

My Christmas story was concluded. I flung down my pen, rose from my desk; and began to pace up and down the room.

It was night, and outside the snowstorm whirled through the air. Strange sounds reached my ears as of soft whispers, or of sighs, that penetrated from the street through the walls of my little chamber, three-fourths of which were engulfed in dark shadows. It was the snow driven by the wind that came crunching against the walls and lashed the window-panes. A light, white, indefinite object scurried past my window and disappeared, leaving a cold shiver within my soul.

I approached the window, looked out upon the street, and leaned my head, heated with the strained effort of imagination, upon the cold frame. The street lay in deserted silence. Now and then the wind ripped up little transparent clouds of snow from the pavement and sent them flying through the air like shreds of a delicate white fabric. A lamp burned opposite my window. Its flame trembled and quivered in fierce struggle with the wind. The flaring streak of light projected like a broadsword into the air, and the snow that was drifted from the roof of the house into this streak of light became aglow for a moment like a scintillating robe of sparks. My heart grew sad and chill as I watched this play of the wind. I quickly undressed myself, put out the lamp and lay down to sleep.

When the light was extinguished and darkness filled my room the sounds grew more audible and the window stared at me like a great white spot. The ceaseless ticking of the clock marked the passing of the seconds. At times their swift onward rush was drowned in the wheezing and crunching of the snow, but soon I heard again the low beat of the seconds as they dropped into eternity.

Occasionally their sound was as distinct and precise as if the clock stood in my own skull.

I lay in my bed and thought of the story that I had just completed, wondering whether it had come out a success.

In this story I told of two beggars, a blind old man and his wife, who in silent, timid retirement trod the path of life that offered them nothing but fear and humiliation. They had left their village on the morning before Christmas to collect alms in the neighbouring settlements that they might on the day thereafter celebrate the birth of Christ in holiday fashion.

They expected to visit the nearest villages and to be back home for the early morning service, with their bags filled with all kinds of crumbs doled out to them for the sake of Christ.

Their hopes (thus I proceeded in my narration) were naturally disappointed. The gifts they received were scanty, and it was very late when the pair, worn out with the day's tramp, finally decided to return to their cold, desolate clay hut. With light burdens on their shoulders and with heavy grief in their hearts, they slowly trudged along over the snow-covered plain, the old woman walking in front and the old man holding fast to her belt and following behind. The night was dark, clouds covered the sky, and for two old people the way to the village was still very long. Their feet sank into the snow and the wind whirled it up and drove it into their faces. Silently and trembling with cold they plodded on and on. Weary and blinded by the snow, the old woman had strayed from the path, and they were now wandering aimlessly across the valley out on the open field.

"Are we going to be home soon? Take care that we do not miss the early mass!" mumbled the blind man behind his wife's weary shoulders.

She said that they would soon be home, and a new shiver of cold passed through her body. She knew she had lost the way, but she dared not tell her husband. At times it seemed to her as if the wind carried the sound of the barking dogs to her ears, and she turned in the direction whence those sounds came; but soon she heard the barking from the other side.

At length her powers gave way and she said to the old man, "Forgive me, father, forgive me for the sake of Christ. I have strayed from the road and I cannot go further. I must sit down."

"You will freeze to death," he answered.

"Let me rest only for a little while. And even if we do freeze to death, what matter it? Surely our life on this earth is not sweet."

The old man heaved a heavy sigh and consented.

They sat down on the snow with their backs against each other and looked like two bundles of rags—the sport of the wind. It drifted clouds of snow against them, covered them up with sharp, pointed crystals, and the old woman, who was more lightly dressed than her husband, soon felt herself in the embrace of a rare, delicious warmth.

"Mother," called the blind man, who shivered with violent cold, "stand up, we must be going!"

But she had dozed off and muttered but half-intelligible words through her sleep. He endeavoured to raise her but he could not for want of adequate strength.

"You will freeze!" he shouted, and then he called aloud for help into the wide open field.

But she felt so warm, so comfortable! After some vain endeavour the blind man sat down again on the snow in dumb desperation. He was now firmly convinced that all that happened to him was by the express will of God and that there was no escape for him and his aged wife. The wind whirled and danced around them in wanton frolic, playfully bestrewed them with snow and had a merry, roguish sport with the tattered garments that covered their old limbs, weary with a long life of pinching destitution. The old man also was now overcome with a feeling of delicious comfort and warmth.

Suddenly the wind wafted the sweet, solemn, melodious sounds of a bell to his ears.

"Mother!" he cried, starting back, "they are ringing for matins. Quick, let us go!"

But she had already gone whence there is no return.

"Do you hear? They are ringing, I say. Get up! Oh, we will be too late!"

He tried to rise, but he found that he could not move. Then he understood that his end was near and he began to pray silently:

"Lord, be gracious unto the souls of your servants! We were sinners, both. Forgive us, oh, Lord! Have mercy upon us!"

Then it seemed to him that from across the field, enveloped in a bright, sparkling snow-cloud, a radiant temple of God was floating toward him—a rare, wondrous temple. It was all made of flaming hearts of men and itself had the likeness of a heart, and in the midst of it, upon an elevated pedestal, stood Christ in his own person. At this vision the old man arose and fell upon his knees on the threshold of the temple. He regained his sight again and he looked at the Saviour and Redeemer. And from his elevated position Christ spoke in a sweet, melodious voice:

"Hearts aglow with pity are the foundation of my temple. Enter thou into my temple, thou who in thy life has thirsted for pity, thou who hast suffered misfortune and humiliation, go to thy Eternal Peace!"

"O, Lord!" spoke the old man, restored to sight, weeping with rapturous joy, "is it Thou in truth, O Lord!"

And Christ smiled benignly upon the old man and his life companion, who was awakened to life again by the smile of the Saviour.

And thus both the beggars froze to death out in the open, snow-covered field.

I brought back to my mind the various incidents of the story, and wondered whether it had come out smooth and touching enough to arouse the reader's pity. It seemed to me that I could answer the question in the affirmative, that it could not possibly fail to produce the effect at which I had aimed.

With this thought I fell asleep, well satisfied with myself. The clock continued to tick, and I heard in my sleep the chasing and roaring of the snowstorm, that grew more and more violent. The lantern was blown out. The storm outside produced ever new sounds. The window shutters clattered. The branches of the trees near the door knocked against the metal plate of the roof. There was a sighing, groaning, howling, roaring and whistling, and all this was now united into a woeful melody that filled the heart with sadness, now into a soft, low strain like a cradle song. It had the effect of a fantastic tale that held the soul as if under a spell.

But suddenly—what was this? The faint spot of the window flamed up into a bluish, phosphorescent light, and the window grew larger and larger until it finally assumed the proportions of the wall. In the blue light which filled the room there appeared of a sudden a thick, white cloud in which bright sparks glowed as with countless eyes. As if whirled about by the wind, the cloud turned and twisted, began to dissolve, became more and more transparent, broke into tiny pieces, and breathed a frosty chill into my body that filled me with anxiety. Something like a dissatisfied, angry mumble proceeded from the shreds of cloud that gained more and more definite shape and assumed forms familiar to my eye. Yonder in the corner were a swarm of children, or rather the shades of children, and behind them emerged a gray-bearded old man by the side of several female forms.

"Whence do these shades come? What do they wish?" were the questions that passed through my mind as I gazed affrighted at this strange apparition.

"Whence come we and whence are we?" was the solemn retort of a serious, stern voice. "Do you not know us? Think a little!"

I shook my head in silence. I did not know them. They kept floating through the air in rhythmic motion as if they led a solemn dance to the tune of the storm. Half transparent, scarcely discernible in their outlines, they wavered lightly and noiselessly around me, and suddenly I distinguished in their midst the blind old man who held on fast to the belt of his old wife. Deeply bent they limped past me, their eyes fixed upon me with a reproachful look.

"Do you recognize them now?" asked the same solemn voice. I did not know whether it was the voice of the storm or the voice of my conscience, but there was in it a tone of command that brooked no contradictions.

"Yes, this is who they are," continued the Voice, "the sad heroes of your successful story. All the others are also heroes of your Christmas stories—children, men and women whom you made to freeze to death in order to amuse the public. See how many there are and how pitiful they look, the offspring of your fancy!"

A movement passed through the wavering forms and two children, a boy and a girl, appeared in the foreground. They looked like two flowers of snow or of the sheen of the moon.

"These children," spoke the Voice, "you have caused to freeze under the window of that rich house in which beamed the brilliant Christmas tree. They were looking at the tree—do you recollect?—and they froze."

Noiselessly my poor little heroes floated past me and disappeared. They seemed to dissolve in the blue, nebulous glare of light. In their place appeared a woman with a sorrowful, emaciated countenance.

"This is that poor woman who was hurrying to her village home on Christmas Eve to bring her children some cheap Christmas gifts. You have let her freeze to death also."

I gazed full of shame and fear at the shade of the woman. She also vanished, and new forms appeared in their turn. They were all sad, silent phantoms with an expression of unspeakable woe in their somber gaze.

And again I heard the solemn Voice speak in sustained, impassive accents:

"WHY have you written these stories? Is there not enough of real, tangible and visible misery in the world that you must needs invent more misery and sorrow, and strain your imagination in order to paint pictures of thrilling, realistic effects? Why do you do this? What is your object? Do you wish to deprive man of all joy in life, do you wish to take from him the last drop of faith in the good, by painting for him only the evil? Why is it that in your Christmas stories year after year you cause to freeze to death now children, now grown-up people? Why? What is your aim?"

I was staggered by this strange indictment. Everybody writes Christmas stories according to the same formula. "You take a poor boy or a poor girl, or something of that sort, and let them freeze somewhere under a window, behind which there is usually a Christmas tree that throws its radiant splendour upon them. This has become the fashion, and I was following the fashion," I answered accordingly.

"If I let these people freeze," I said, "I do it with the best object in the world. By painting their death struggle I stir up humane feelings in the public for these unfortunates. I want to move the heart of my reader, that is all."

A strange agitation passed through the throng of phantoms, as if they wished to raise a mocking protest against my words.

"Do you see how they are laughing?" said the mysterious Voice.

"Why are they laughing?" I asked in a scarcely audible tone.

"Because you speak so foolishly. You wish to arouse noble feelings in the hearts of men by your pictures of imagined misery, when real misery and suffering are nothing to them but a daily spectacle. Consider for how long a time people have endeavoured to stir up noble feelings in the hearts of men, think of how many men before you have applied their genius to that end, and then cast a look into real life! Fool that you are! If the reality does not move them, and if their feelings are not offended by its cruel, ruthless misery, and by the fathomless abyss of actual wretchedness, then how can you hope that the fictions of your imagination will make them better? Do you really think that you can move the heart of a human being by telling him about a frozen child? The sea of misery breaks against the dam of heartlessness, it rages and surges against it, and you want to appease it by throwing a few peas into it!"

The phantoms accompanied these words with their silent laughter, and the storm laughed a shrill, cynical laugh; but the Voice continued to speak unceasingly. Each word that it spoke was like a nail driven into my brain. It became intolerable, and I could no longer hold out.

"It is all a lie, a lie!" I cried in a paroxysm of rage, and jumping from my bed I fell headlong into the dark, and sank more and more quickly, more and more deeply, into the gaping abyss that suddenly opened before me. The whistling, howling, roaring and laughing followed me downward and the phantoms chased me through the dark, grinned in my face and mocked at me.

I awoke in the morning with a violent headache and in a very bad humour. The first thing I did was to read over my story of the blind beggar and his wife once more, and then I tore the manuscript into pieces.

A
Gingerbread
House

from

THE GENTLE ART OF COOKERY

This recipe for a gingerbread house comes from an old, very English cookbook called The Gentle Art of Cookery. *The "gentle art," as it turns out, is really rather rigid, like a good old English matron: "this must be done so…and this…just so." Also, please note: the posture of your "little gingerbread woman" standing at the door of your gingerbread house should be straight-backed and eyes forward. A little red and green sprinkling on the icing might add to the Christmas theme.*

Gingerbread

The joy of the old-fashioned gingerbread, sold at every English fair was, of course, the fact that it was fashioned into enchanting shapes of animals and human beings; for choice, kings and queens in gilded crowns. But the expression, "the gilt is off the gingerbread" has outlived, in England, the custom of giving gingerbread so romantic a form.

In Holland, for weeks before St. Nicholas' Day, December 6th, the windows of every baker's shop are filled with gingerbread in every strange device from figures of the children's Saint himself to that of little animals, donkeys, rabbits and bears. Some of these cakes are two feet long, and of all sizes.

Even the most blasé modern child feels the fascination of these fantastic delicacies, and they are very easily made. Here is the recipe:

Two pounds of flour, a quarter of a pound of brown sugar, one ounce of ground ginger, two ounces of candied peel, half an ounce of carraway seeds, half an ounce of cinnamon, a quarter of a pound of butter, two ounces of hot treacle.

Mix the dry ingredients well together, then cream the butter and mix well, add the hot treacle. Knead it into a thick paste. If it is too stiff, moisten it with a very little milk. The paste must be very smooth. Roll it out thin and cut it into any shape, making any design upon it with the back of a knife. The shape of the gingerbread need be limited only by the skill or fancy of the artist. Fishes are easy to draw, so are birds, and pigs, and elephants, and humans in Anglo-Saxon attitudes.

Bake them till they are crisp all through.

A Gingerbread House

A "Gingerbread House" is an old-fashioned Christmas treat that is worth making for the delight of nurseries where the children are not too blasé; if the children are allowed to help to make it no child will be too modern to enjoy it.

The pattern for the little house must be cut out first in paper. Each of the four sides of the house must be made separately, and the sections of the roof which should have two gables if it is to be firm; therefore the front and back walls of the house must have two points to support the sections of the roof. Thus:—

Then doors and windows must be drawn on the paper, according to the architectural tastes of the designer. When the four walls and the four sections of the roof are cut out in paper, the paper must be laid on the rolled-out paste, which must be carefully cut out. Then it is baked. When it is cooked and hard the little house must be fitted together and cemented with white of egg. It should stand on a pastry board or any convenient equivalent. A little chimney should be added, and a gingerbread wall round a little garden. Then there must be icing on the roof for snow, and icing in the little garden, in which bunches of raisins will stand as trees. This "snow" will help the gingerbread wall or railings to stand up. At the door of the cottage should be a little gingerbread woman.

The old-fashioned way of illuminating the house was to put a night-light inside. But in these days, when Christmas trees are lit with electric light, probably something could be done with an electric lamp in the little house, for a night-light was apt to give the gingerbread a smoky flavour—not that the children who ate it minded that, for the end of the little house is to be demolished and eaten.

The
Thieves Who Couldn't Help Sneezing

by
THOMAS HARDY
(1840–1928)

"The Thieves Who Couldn't Help Sneezing" is one of Hardy's rare stories written for children, and (I think) his only Christmas story. I suppose he had other more serious matters to attend to. This is regrettable, for he has a fine comic touch, and an understanding of country and festive traditions that would do well for readers of any age.

Many years ago, when oak trees now past their prime were about as large as elderly gentlemen's walking-sticks, there lived in Wessex a yeoman's son, whose name was Hubert. He was about fourteen years of age, and was as remarkable for his candour and lightness of heart as for his physical courage, of which, indeed, he was a little vain.

One cold Christmas Eve his father, having no other help at hand, sent him on an important errand to a small town several miles from home. He travelled on horseback, and was detained by the business till a late hour of the evening. At last, however, it was completed; he returned to the inn, the horse was saddled, and he started on his way. His journey homeward lay through the Vale of Blackmore, a fertile but somewhat lonely district, with heavy clay roads and crooked lanes. In those days, too, a great part of it was thickly wooded.

It must have been about nine o'clock when, riding along amid the overhanging trees upon his stout-legged cob, Jerry, and singing a Christmas carol, to be in harmony with the season, Hubert fancied that he heard a noise among the boughs. This recalled to his mind that the spot he was traversing bore an evil name. Men had been waylaid there. He looked at Jerry, and wished he had been of any other colour than light grey; for on this account the docile animal's form was visible even here in the dense shade. "What do I care?" he said aloud, after a few minutes of reflection. "Jerry's legs are too nimble to allow any highwayman to come near me."

"Ha! ha! indeed," was said in a deep voice; and the next moment a man darted from the thicket on his right hand, another man from the thicket on his left hand, and another from a tree-trunk a few yards ahead. Hubert's bridle was seized, he was pulled from his horse, and although he struck out with all his might, as a brave boy would naturally do, he was overpowered. His arms were tied behind him, his legs bound tightly together, and he was thrown into a ditch. The robbers, whose faces he could now dimly perceive to be artificially blackened, at once departed, leading off the horse.

As soon as Hubert had a little recovered himself, he found that by great exertion he was able to extricate his legs from the cord; but, in spite of every endeavour, his arms remained bound as fast as before. All, therefore, that he could do was to rise to his feet and proceed on his way with his arms behind him, and trust to chance for getting them unfastened. He knew that it would be impossible to reach home on foot that night, and in such a condition; but he walked on. Owing to the confusion which this attack caused in his brain, he lost his way, and would have been inclined to lie down and rest till morning among the dead leaves had he not known the danger of sleeping without wrappers in a frost so severe. So he wandered farther onwards, his arms wrung and numbed by the cord which pinioned him, and his heart aching for the loss of poor Jerry, who never had been known to kick, or bite, or show a single vicious habit. He was not a little glad when he discerned through the trees a distant light. Towards this he made his way, and presently found himself in front of a large mansion with flanking wings, gables, and towers, the battlements and chimneys showing their shapes against the stars.

All was silent; but the door stood wide open, it being from this door that the light shone which had attracted him. On entering he found himself in a vast apartment arranged as a dining-hall, and brilliantly illuminated. The walls were covered with a great deal of dark wainscoting, formed into moulded panels, carvings, closet-doors, and the usual fittings of a house of that kind. But what drew his attention most was the large table in the midst of the hall, upon which was spread a sumptuous supper, as yet untouched. Chairs were placed around, and it appeared as if something had occurred to interrupt the meal just at the time when all were ready to begin.

Even had Hubert been so inclined, he could not have eaten in his helpless state, unless by dipping his mouth into the dishes, like a pig or cow. He wished first to obtain assistance; and was about to penetrate farther into the house for that purpose when he heard hasty footsteps in the porch and the words, "Be quick!" uttered in the deep voice which had reached him when he was dragged from the horse. There was only just time for him to dart under the table before three men entered the dining-hall. Peeping from beneath the hanging edges of the tablecloth, he perceived that their faces, too, were blackened, which at once removed any doubts he may have felt that these were the same thieves.

"Now, then," said the first—the man with the deep voice— "let us hide ourselves. They will all be back again in a minute. That was a good trick to get them out of the house—eh?"

"Yes. You well imitated the cries of a man in distress," said the second.

"Excellently," said the third.

"But they will soon find out that it was a false alarm. Come, where shall we hide? It must be some place we can stay in for two or three hours, till all are in bed and asleep. Ah! I have it. Come this way! I have learnt that the farther cupboard is not opened once in a twelve-month; it will serve our purpose exactly."

The speaker advanced into a corridor which led from the hall. Creeping a little farther forward, Hubert could discern that the cupboard stood at the end, facing the dining-hall. The thieves entered it, and closed the door. Hardly breathing, Hubert glided forward, to learn a little more of their intention, if possible; and, coming close, he could hear the robbers whispering about the different rooms where the jewels, plate, and other valuables of the house were kept, which they plainly meant to steal.

They had not been long in hiding when a gay chattering of ladies and gentlemen was audible on the terrace without. Hubert felt that it would not do to be caught prowling about the house, unless he wished to be taken for a robber himself, and stood in a dark corner of the porch, where he could see everything without

being himself seen. In a moment or two a whole troop of per-
sonages came gliding past him into the house. There were an
elderly gentleman and lady, eight or nine young ladies, as many
young men, besides half a dozen menservants and maids. The
mansion had apparently been quite emptied of its occupants.

"Now, children and young people, we will resume our meal,"
said the old gentleman. "What the noise could have been I cannot understand. I never felt so certain in my life that there was a
person being murdered outside my door."

Then the ladies began saying how frightened they had been,
and how they had expected an adventure, and how it had ended
in nothing at all.

"Wait a while," said Hubert to himself. "You'll have adventure
enough by-and-by, ladies."

It appeared that the young men and women were married
sons and daughters of the old couple, who had come that day to
spend Christmas with their parents.

The door was then closed, Hubert being left outside in the
porch. He thought this a proper moment for asking their assistance; and, since he was unable to knock with his hands, began
boldly to kick the door.

"Hullo! What disturbance are you making here?" said a foot-
man who opened it; and, seizing Hubert by the shoulder, he
pulled him into the dining-hall. "Here's a strange boy I have
found making a noise in the porch, Sir Simon."

Everybody turned.

"Bring him forward," said Sir Simon, the old gentleman
before mentioned. "What were you doing there, my boy?"

"Why, his arms are tied!" said one of the ladies.

"Poor fellow!" said another.

Hubert at once began to explain that he had been waylaid on
his journey home, robbed of his horse, and mercilessly left in
this condition by the thieves.

"Only to think of it!" exclaimed Sir Simon.

"That's a likely story," said one of the gentlemen-guests,
incredulously.

"Doubtful, hey?" asked Sir Simon.

"Perhaps he's a robber himself," suggested a lady.

"There is a curiously wild wicked look about him, certainly, now that I examine him closely," said the old mother.

Hubert blushed with shame; and, instead of continuing his story, and relating that robbers were concealed in the house, he doggedly held his tongue, and half resolved to let them find out their danger for themselves.

"Well, untie him," said Sir Simon. "Come, since it is Christmas Eve, we'll treat him well. Here, my lad; sit down in that empty seat at the bottom of the table, and make as good a meal as you can. When you have had your fill we will listen to more particulars of your story."

The feast then proceeded; and Hubert, now at liberty, was not at all sorry to join in. The more they ate and drank the merrier did the company become; the wine flowed freely, the logs flared up the chimney, the ladies laughed at the gentlemen's stories; in short, all went as noisily and as happily as a Christmas gathering in old times possibly could do.

Hubert, in spite of his hurt feelings at their doubts of his honesty, could not help being warmed both in mind and in body by the good cheer, the scene, and the example of hilarity set by his neighbours. At last he laughed as heartily at their stories and repartees as the old Baronet, Sir Simon, himself. When the meal was almost over one of the sons, who had drunk a little too much wine, after the manner of men in that century, said to Hubert, "Well, my boy, how are you? Can you take a pinch of snuff?" He held out one of the snuff-boxes which were then becoming common among young and old throughout the country.

"Thank you," said Hubert, accepting a pinch.

"Tell the ladies who you are, what you are made of, and what you can do," the young man continued, slapping Hubert upon the shoulder.

"Certainly," said our hero, drawing himself up, and thinking it best to put a bold face on the matter. "I am a travelling magician."

"Indeed!"

"What shall we hear next?"

"Can you call up spirits from the vasty deep, young wizard?"

"I can conjure up a tempest in a cupboard," Hubert replied.

"Ha-ha!" said the old Baronet, pleasantly rubbing his hands.

"We must see this performance. Girls, don't go away: here's something to be seen."

"Not dangerous, I hope?" said the old lady.

Hubert rose from the table. "Hand me your snuff-box, please," he said to the young man who had made free with him. "And now," he continued, "without the least noise, follow me. If any of you speak it will break the spell."

They promised obedience. He entered the corridor, and, taking off his shoes, went on tiptoe to the cupboard door, the guests advancing in a silent group at a little distance behind him. Hubert next placed a stool in front of the door, and, by standing upon it, was tall enough to reach the top. He then, just as noiselessly, poured all the snuff from the box along the upper edge of the door, and, with a few short puffs of breath, blew the snuff through the chink into the interior of the cupboard. He held up his finger to the assembly, that they might be silent.

"Dear me, what's that?" said the old lady, after a minute or two had elapsed.

A suppressed sneeze had come from inside the cupboard.

Hubert held up his finger again.

"How very singular," whispered Sir Simon. "This is most interesting."

Hubert took advantage of the moment to gently slide the bolt of the cupboard door into its place. "More snuff," he said, calmly.

"More snuff," said Sir Simon. Two or three gentlemen passed their boxes, and the contents were blown in at the top of the cupboard. Another sneeze, not quite so well suppressed as the first, was heard: then another, which seemed to say that it would not be suppressed under any circumstances whatever. At length there arose a perfect storm of sneezes.

"Excellent, excellent for one so young!" said Sir Simon. "I am much interested in this trick of throwing the voice—called, I believe, ventriloquism."

"More snuff," said Hubert.

"More snuff," said Sir Simon. Sir Simon's man brought a large jar of the best scented Scotch.

Hubert once more charged the upper chink of the cupboard, and blew the snuff into the interior, as before. Again he charged, and again, emptying the whole contents of the jar. The tumult of sneezes became really extraordinary to listen to—there was no cessation. It was like wind, rain, and sea battling in a hurricane.

"I believe there are men inside, and that it is no trick at all!" exclaimed Sir Simon, the truth flashing on him.

"There are," said Hubert. "They are come to rob the house; and they are the same who stole my horse."

The sneezes changed to spasmodic groans. One of the thieves, hearing Hubert's voice, cried, "Oh! mercy! mercy! let us out of this!"

"Where's my horse?" cried Hubert.

"Tied to the tree in the hollow behind Short's Gibbet. Mercy! mercy! let us out, or we shall die of suffocation!"

All the Christmas guests now perceived that this was no longer sport, but serious earnest. Guns and cudgels were procured; all the menservants were called in, and arranged in position outside the cupboard. At a signal Hubert withdrew the bolt, and stood on the defensive. But the three robbers, far from attacking them, were found crouching in the corner, gasping for breath. They made no resistance; and, being pinioned, were placed in an outhouse till the morning.

Hubert now gave the remainder of his story to the assembled company, and was profusely thanked for the services he had rendered. Sir Simon pressed him to stay over the night, and accept the use of the best bedroom the house afforded, which had been occupied by Queen Elizabeth and King Charles successively when on their visits to this part of the country. But Hubert declined, being anxious to find his horse Jerry, and to test the truth of the robbers' statements concerning him.

Several of the guests accompanied Hubert to the spot behind the gibbet, alluded to by the thieves as where Jerry was hidden. When they reached the knoll and looked over, behold! there the horse stood, uninjured, and quite unconcerned. At sight of Hubert he neighed joyfully: and nothing could exceed Hubert's gladness at finding him. He mounted, wished his friends "Good night!" and cantered off in the direction they pointed out, reaching home safely about four o'clock in the morning.

Christmas Kitchen Fifty Years Ago

by
LILLIAN EUGENIA SMITH
(1897–1966)

I don't know of anyone who writes quite so well on the delights of the kitchen of long ago as Lillian Eugenia Smith. Butter-churnings and pecan nuts and clotted cream—and eggs, eggs, eggs. As Smith herself suggests, the warming scents of a childhood Christmas kitchen seep not only into the memory, but into the very bones.

Our old kitchen returns in my memory, decked out in its winter ways. Always as I think about it a fire is burning easy and slow in the fireplace, and one of the cats is sleeping at its edge, and somebody, Big Grandma or Mother or the cook, is rocking in the chair near the cat with a pan on her lap preparing something for dinner or supper.

The kitchen was a big wide room on the southwest side of the house, full of yellow light in the afternoon; and this yellow light always smelled like spice cake, or spareribs slowly browning, or maybe sweet potato pies at the crusty moment of being considered "done" and ready to set out on a long deal table to cool.

In the big black iron stove there was a murmur of wood burning in slow steady combustion, just right for the pies. A woodbox was at the side of the stove stacked with various kinds of wood: resinous kindling for a sudden flame, splintered dry pine for a quick breakfast fire, a little green pine to temper the dry pine, oak split into the proper size and length for the long haul of the four-hour roasting which a fresh ham requires.

Mother and the cook were expert with a wood stove and knew just how to encourage or dampen its ardor by their skilled mixing of kindling and pine and oak and their knowing twist of the damper on the stove pipe, and their subliminal awareness that the time had arrived to shift a pan or kettle from one side of the stove to the other.

I can see my mother now opening the wide oven, putting her hand in to test its temperature, just as she put her lips to our foreheads to see if we had fever. Her sense of warmth was as accurate as any thermometer. I never heard her blame the temperature of the oven for her rare failures with cake. She would lift a layer, weigh it delicately in her hands, and say the cake was "sad" because she had put a little too much sugar in it, or heavy because she had added a smidge too much flour.

We children adored sad cakes; for we could eat at once the fallen stuff, delicious in its extra sweetness and crunchiness. (Mother would not have let it enter her dining room, it would have shamed her too much.)

Beyond the big stove was the kitchen sink. For years there was no actual sink but a long table covered with zinc on which were two or three big dishpans. Dishes were washed in pan Number 1, rinsed in pan Number 2; the pots were soaked in pan Number 3. An orderly procedure. Somebody toted in water from the artesian well in the back yard, and I am sure all nine of us did our share but since I was one of the younger children, this part of it fades out. By the time I was eight, we had "running water," as we called it, in the kitchen, and a real sink, and several bathrooms. But my mother or the cook—perhaps both—was reluctant to give up the old ways entirely, for I remember with eyes more mature than an eight-year-old's that dishwater was carried to the back yard to be poured around certain plants which our mother thought profited from the fine mixture of grease and "richness."

Extending from the far end of the kitchen was a porch latticed in (and later screened) where the screened safes were kept for cooked food and a monstrous-sized icebox our father had had built at his mills. It was made of heavy oak timber, some of it four inches thick; and the whole affair was lined with zinc. To lift its lid was impossible without pulley and chain. I suspect our mother lived in constant fear of a decapitated child. Perhaps that is why only the raw meats and fish and other unappetizing foodstuffs were kept there with the ice.

The milk from our Jersey cow (she gave four gallons a day) was always kept in a special milk-safe screened with cheesecloth (before metal screens were available); and this safe was presided over by my mother, who was not certain where typhoid germs came from but had a canny notion that dirty milk could precipitate a dozen mean ills in addition to the dramatic one of typhoid.

How delicately she skimmed those pans of milk! They were large round shallow pans, chosen because cream can be skimmed more easily from shallow pans. I would stand beside her, sunk deep in a sweet orgy of sensuous delight, as I watched her fold heavy yellow cream back from the pale blue milk beneath, then skillfully swoop the thick roll up with her big spoon into the cream bowl. I'd whisper, "Oh Mama, let's have some hot gingerbread for supper all covered with cream," and she'd look at me and say "Sssh…" as though the cream were a sleeping baby. She handled it as gently as if it were one, just as she handled tender plants when setting them out in the beds she had made for them. But though she said *sssh*, nearly always the hot gingerbread would appear at supper covered with the clotted cream as a special treat for the nine of us.

By the milk-safe, in the corner, was kept the churn where butter was made. Every other day, the grandmothers churned. The earthenware tall churn would be washed with hot water and soap, carefully dried, put by the fireplace near the rocker. The heavy cream was poured in it and quarts of "clabber" (sour milk that had thickened to a delicate firm jelly-like consistency in the unrefrigerated temperature). One of the grandmothers would settle in the rocker and begin her task. *Flop…flop… flop…*the churning made this sound to me as I'd squat there watching. Finally, under the repetitive up-and-down motion, lumps of butter formed and the clabber turned to delicious buttermilk. This chemistry fascinated me. I would beg to understand exactly how it happened. Mother or Dad would talk about emulsion, about fat cells, etc. But this reasonable explanation could not get into my imagination, where the strange wonderful transformation of cream into butter had crawled up beside ghosts and angels and fairies and become an act almost as magic as spinning gold out of straw.

Finally, Big Grandmother gathered the butter into a dish and then beat it and pressed it and beat it and pressed until every drop of milk had been separated from the yellow glistening butter. Then the wooden mold was brought out, the butter packed into it, left there a moment, then eased on to a tray in a half-pound round stamped with a sheaf of wheat on top. When all the half-pounds had been molded, this creation was covered with a snowy white piece of an old tablecloth, or worn-out napkin and laid away in the milk-safe.

In this cavernous, bright, spice-laden kitchen the Christmas preparations began in late November, for the fruit cakes were always made early and set aside in the dark pantry to season.

I don't see how my mother could have managed without the big enameled dishpans at such a time. She'd sit at the wide table alongside Big Granny or Little Granny and the cook cutting orange peel and raisins, citron and ginger and pecans, until one of the pans would be filled with the sticky spicy mess. Then she would measure into another pan flour by the quart and sugar by the pint. She'd leave this, go to the pantry, come back with a basket filled with six or seven dozen eggs. I liked the creamy-brown ones best and would ask to be permitted to count out the two dozen needed. Then Mother would break them, giving each a sharp nip on the edge of the table and depositing its undisturbed contents, freed of the shell, into the pan. The whole affair was elegant: golden orbs of eggs floating in islands of white... Mother's quick, dexterous movements as she went about her work...everything calmly moving toward the creation she was intent on. She was an artist in her own kitchen and there was a deep pleasure in her eyes as she gently pushed prying little ones away, and went on with her creating.

The day came when I must have my try at breaking an egg—which, somewhere in me, had become almost as taboo as setting fire to the house or flinging one of her Haviland china plates to the floor. But now I was seven and grown up enough to try and she gave her permission. I stood trembling for five minutes on the edge of that precipice before I could take the fatal step. But I took it. I cracked the egg. Then hesitating again, I brought on disaster by spilling the egg on the floor. But Mother did not scold: she said, It happens; let's clean it up. We cleaned it up. Then she said, Try again. And I tried again and did it. And I am not sure any triumph in my life ever pleased me more than that successful act.

Now, over the fruit and nuts, were sprinkled cinnamon and nutmeg and mace and a little grated lemon peel. The nuts and fruit and flour and sugar and eggs were finally mixed well together in the biggest pan of all. Someone had greased the four-inch-deep cake pans and lined them with brown paper and now they were filled and placed in shallow biscuit tins lined with a half-inch of water for the slow steam-baking they required.

But for me, the making of fruit cake never quite reached the mouth-watering excitement of watching our mother do her famous turkey dressing. To experience this involved your glands, senses, mind, heart and soul.

It took place on Christmas morning. And no matter how absorbed I might be with new dolls and new books I'd be on hand to witness this great spectacle:

First, she crushed the contents of a dozen or more boxes of Uneeda Biscuits in a deep bowl. On these crushed crackers she then poured the "essence" which had resulted from browning and simmering for two hours the neck, liver, gizzard and wing tips of the twenty-eight-pound turkey. If the essence did not dampen the crackers sufficiently—and it never did—she then "stole," as she said, three or four cups of the most delicious-smelling stock from the turkey roasting pan and added to the mixture. This stealing always sent me into giggles but I'd keep glancing up at her face to be sure she was joking, for unlike my father she joked rarely and when she did, she joked so drily that we were never quite sure she meant it as a joke. Anyway, after the theft of the turkey stock, she put in the dressing six or seven cups of finely chopped celery, a few celery seeds, salt, pepper, a little chipped onion (not much), a half-pound of homemade butter (depending on the richness of the essence) and two dozen eggs. This was well stirred, then two quarts of pecans were added, and two quarts of oysters and a cupful or so of oyster liquor. The whole thing was now stirred for five minutes or more, tasted, a little sage added, a mite more pepper, and then after staring hard at it, Mother would go to the stove, pick up the kettle and pour a bit of steaming water into the pan to soften it a little more. This was IT. Mother then pushed some of it into the turkey pan—not much, for the turkey was cooking and already had a sausage stuffing in it. Then, after looking at it again for a long moment, and tasting it once more, she poured this delicious mess into deep baking dishes and set it aside to be cooked for thirty or forty minutes shortly before dinner. When served, it would be firm but fluffy, with just enough crispy bits of pecans and succulent oysters.

By this time, the big sisters had filled silver dishes with candies and nuts and stuffed dates, and glass dishes were filled with homemade pickles and olives; somebody was stuffing the celery with cheese and someone else was easing the jellied cranberry sauce into one of Mother's fancy flutey porcelain dishes. The cook, or perhaps Big Grandma, had prepared the sweet potatoes for candying and they were now on the back of the stove gently simmering in water, sugar, butter, orange peel and cinnamon. The rice would be cooked during the last twenty-two minutes before the dinner bell was rung, but already the gravy had been made and thickened with chipped-up liver, gizzard, and hard-boiled eggs.

The pork salad and Waldorf salad, made early, were kept in the ice-cold pantry until just before dinner when they were placed on the sideboard in two hand-painted bowls. Also on the sideboard were fruit cake, caramel cake, six-layered coconut cake, Lord Baltimore cake, lemon-cheese cake, and several coconut pies. Our father always ate a slice of coconut pie but the rest of us preferred the traditional ambrosia for Christmas dessert, with a sampling of all the cakes.

Since the Greeks there have been ambrosias and ambrosias. Ours was fit for the most exacting Olympian taste, for it was of a special delicacy since the oranges were not sliced but each plug of fruit lifted out of its inner skin and kept as nearly whole as possible. A layer of these fragile orange plugs would be put in the bowl, then a layer of finely grated fresh coconut (not shredded), then a sprinkling of sugar, then another layer of orange, coconut, and so on until the bowl was full. It might have tasted better served to you as you reclined on a floating cloud but I doubt it.

And now, the dinner bell rang and in we ran, already too stuffed by our nibblings since five A.M. to do more than admire, sniff, and taste here and there. But no matter how poked-out I was I made a miracle somehow and pushed in two helpings of turkey dressing. The other things could wait until tomorrow or the next day or the next.

All of this was unforgettable, seeping not only into memory but into bones and glands.

But even Christmas Week did not delight the palate more than did hog-killing week. I still am not sure whether turkey dressing, even my mother's, won a clear victory over liver-'n'-lights stew. The stew was cooked two days on the back of the stove, spiced with onions, black pepper and salt and a clove or two, and seasoned with bits of fatty-lean pork.

First, the liver and lights (lungs) and sweetbreads of a hog were cut into small pieces and browned with the bits of fatty-lean pork, in an enormous black iron kettle. Water was then added, and the kettle pushed back on the stove where it could cook slowly, after the onions and black pepper and salt were added. At the end of two days of slow simmering, this delicacy was ready to eat. We liked it best with hot fluffy cornbread or with grits. I have often wondered why we cannot have it, today. Is it necessary to kill one's own hogs in order to enjoy what is surely one of the most delicious of provincial dishes?

Of course, along with the liver-'n'-lights stew came the fresh-made sausage (with just the right amount of sage and red pepper and fat) for breakfast; and roasted spareribs, a few nights later, for supper. And the following week we were likely to have backbone and rice for dinner.

And now suddenly, because it is winter in the memory, one smells oysters roasting in the shells. This roast took place in the back yard on a circular sheet-iron saw which our father had sent from the mill, and under which a fire was made. The greedy memory of childhood holds it all: oysters and turkey dressing and liver-'n'-lights and pork salad and pecans and ambrosia: food that enhanced childhood Christmases and becomes now a mouth-watering memory that returns each winter of one's life, however far away the old kitchen may be.

For our family, it is gone forever. We are left only with its smells and sounds and tastes, and a few "receipts" of the family's traditional dishes.

Some of these I shall write down here. Remember, they are not accurately measured and weighed. Our kitchen was no laboratory, it was a gourmet's studio where the artist played the major role; an artist whose hand was so sensitized to quantity and weight and the eye to appearances that scales and cups were often laid aside—except for the making of cakes. But all real cooks know about pinches and smidges, and a fluff of this, a dusting of that, so perhaps these old receipts will not be a puzzlement to them.

The Famous Turkey Dressing

We made it in my childhood with Uneeda Biscuits, but I find unsalted crisp plain crackers of any brand as good.

For six people, four cups of crushed crackers should be sufficient. Boil neck, liver, gizzard (after browning in a little butter) for at least two hours or until tender; add water now and then, if necessary. You should have two cups of strong stock, seasoned with salt and pepper and two stalks of celery. Remove the celery and add stock to the crackers. Then add two cups of diced fresh celery; one cup of nuts, one cup of oysters. A half-cup of oyster liquor will improve this mixture. Chip a small amount of onion—no more than half a teaspoonful—add a skimpy bit of garlic (if you like) but no more than a bare suggestion (one half a small bud, chipped). Add a pinch of thyme, a pinch of sage. I usually add a few sliced ripe olives and a few mushrooms, which I think enhance the flavor. Now, as did my mother, "steal" a little rich stock out of the turkey pan—as much as you can spare, taking care that you leave plenty for gravy. Add three eggs and stir several minutes. You should now have a soft, not soupy, mixture. If you do not, add a bit of hot water. Or if too soupy, add a slice of broken-up bread, or a few more crackers. Now put in as much butter as your family's health can take. A large tablespoon is plenty for my modern taste. It should melt in the warm mixture as you stir.

The dressing is ready now for your casseroles and should fill two small ones or one large one. Let it stand an hour, then cook 30 minutes; keep warm for dinner.

Christmas Ambrosia

Ambrosia is made of tender oranges and freshly grated coconut, sprinkled with enough sugar to make it delicately sweet. Peel oranges, use sharp knife to get off most of the skin of the fruit, then slip the plugs of fruit out whole when you can. A layer of orange, a layer of grated coconut, a sprinkling of sugar, then another layer, still another until your bowl is full. It improves when allowed to set for a few hours, or even overnight, in a cool place.

Sweet Potato Pone, Fancied Up

This is not for Christmas but it is a hearty winter dessert to try now and then.

You grate the raw sweet potatoes. Since size and texture of sweet potatoes differ, it is hard for me to give you here the proper measurements. Let's try three cups of grated raw sweet potato; add to this three cups of milk, and three well-beaten eggs. Put in a dusting of nutmeg. Add a cup of pale brown sugar. (Taste: do not have too sweet.) Pour into a baking pan. (It should be about an inch and a half thick.) Cook slowly in the oven, much as you would bake a sweet potato. Begin it at a heat of 400, turn to 325 for the rest of the time. An hour should be about right. Serve this with clotted cream—if you have such—or with whipped cream. Add pecans if desired.

Pork Salad

I doubt that many people would dare eat it in this day of cholesterol doubts, etc., but it was powerful good, and it never made one of the little Smiths ill. First, you baked a fresh pork ham. And, perhaps, had one meal from it. You then cut the lean meat into small pieces (about three cups for six to eight people). You diced a cupful of celery, a cupful of apple, and added this to the mixture. You also added pecans cut small. You seasoned this with a homemade cooked salad dressing which had plenty of vinegar in it. This is it; and it is good. Especially when served with pickled peaches.

The *Shepherd*

by
FREDERICK FORSYTH
(1938–   )

I've been reading Frederick Forsyth's story of "The Shepherd" on CBC radio every Christmas Eve for more than fifteen years. And every year the listeners call. It has become for me, and for many of the faithful, a part of the Christmas tradition. A story where all the pieces fit, and all the pieces fall. My cap off to Frederick Forsyth.

For a brief moment, while waiting for the control tower to clear me for takeoff, I glanced out through the Perspex cockpit canopy at the surrounding German countryside. It lay white and crisp beneath the crackling December moon.

Behind me lay the boundary fence of the Royal Air Force base, and beyond the fence, as I had seen while swinging my little fighter into line with the takeoff runway, the sheet of snow covering the flat farmland stretched away to the line of the pine trees, two miles distant in the night yet so clear I could almost see the shapes of the trees themselves.

Ahead of me, as I waited for the voice of the controller to come through the headphones, was the runway itself, a slick black ribbon of tarmac, flanked by twin rows of bright-burning lights, illuminating the solid path cut earlier by the snowplows. Behind the lights were the humped banks of the morning's snow, frozen hard once again where the snowplow blades had pushed them. Far away to my right, the airfield tower stood up like a single glowing candle amid the brilliant hangars where the muffled aircraftmen were even now closing down the station for the night.

Inside the control tower, I knew, all was warmth and merriment, the staff waiting only for my departure to close down also, jump into the waiting cars, and head back to the parties in the mess. Within minutes of my going, the lights would die out, leaving only the huddled hangars, seeming hunched against the bitter night, the shrouded fighter planes, the sleeping fuel-bowser trucks, and, above them all, the single flickering station light, brilliant red above the black-and-white airfield, beating out in Morse code the name of the station—CELLE—to an unheeding sky. For tonight there would be no wandering aviators to look down and check their bearings; tonight was Christmas Eve, in the year of grace 1957, and I was a young pilot trying to get home to Blighty for his Christmas leave.

I was in a hurry and my watch read ten-fifteen by the dim blue glow of the control panel where the rows of dials quivered and danced. It was warm and snug inside the cockpit, the heating turned up full to prevent the Perspex' icing up. It was like a cocoon, small and warm and safe, shielding me from the bitter cold outside, from the freezing night that can kill a man inside a minute if he is exposed to it at six hundred miles an hour.

"Charlie Delta…"

The controller's voice woke me from my reverie, sounding in my headphones as if he were with me in the tiny cockpit, shouting in my ear. He's had a jar or two already, I thought. Strictly against orders, but what the hell? It's Christmas Eve.

"Charlie Delta… Control," I responded.

"Charlie Delta, clear takeoff," he said.

I saw no point in responding. I simply eased the throttle forward slowly with the left hand, holding the Vampire steady down the central line with the right hand. Behind me the low whine of the Goblin engine rose and rose, passing through a cry and into a scream. The snub-nosed fighter rolled, the lights each side of the runway passed in ever quicker succession, till they were flashing in a continuous blur. She became light, the nose rose fractionally, freeing the nosewheel from contact with the runway, and the rumble vanished instantly. Seconds later the main wheels came away and their soft drumming also stopped. I held her low above the deck, letting the speed build up till a glance at the air-speed indicator told me we were through 120 knots and heading for 150. As the end of the runway whizzed beneath my feet I pulled the Vampire into a gently climbing turn to the left, easing up the undercarriage lever as I did so.

From beneath and behind me I heard the dull clunk of the wheels entering their bays and felt the lunge forward of the jet as the drag of the undercarriage vanished. In front of me the three red lights representing three wheels extinguished themselves. I held her into the climbing turn, pressing the radio button with the left thumb.

"Charlie Delta, clear airfield, wheels up and locked," I said into my oxygen mask.

"Charlie Delta, roger, over to Channel D," said the controller, and then, before I could change radio channels, he added, "Happy Christmas."

Strictly against the rules of radio procedure, of course. I was very young then, and very conscientious. But I replied, "Thank you, Tower, and same to you." Then I switched channels to tune into the RAF's North Germany Air Control frequency.

Down on my right thigh was strapped the map with my course charted on it in blue ink, but I did not need it. I knew the details by heart, worked out earlier with the navigation officer in the nav. hut. Turn overhead Celle airfield onto course 265 degrees, continue climbing to 27,000 feet. On reaching height, maintain course and keep speed to 485 knots. Check in with Channel D to let them know you're in their airspace, then a straight run over the Dutch coast south of the Bevelands into the North Sea. After forty-four minutes' flying time, change to Channel F and call Lakenheath Control to give you a "steer." Fourteen minutes later you'll be overhead Lakenheath. After that, follow instructions and they'll bring you down on a radio-controlled descent. No problem, all routine procedures. Sixty-six minutes' flying time, with the descent and landing, and the Vampire had enough fuel for over eighty minutes in the air.

Swinging over Celle airfield at 5,000 feet, I straightened up and watched the needle on my compass settle happily down on a course of 265 degrees. The nose was pointing toward the black, freezing vault of the night sky, studded with stars so brilliant they flickered their white fire against the eyeballs. Below, the black-and-white map of north Germany was growing smaller, the dark masses of the pine forests blending into the white expanses of the fields. Here and there a village or small town glittered with lights. Down there amid the gaily lit streets the carol singers would be out, knocking on the holly-studded doors to sing "Silent Night" and collect *pfennigs* for charity. The Westphalian housewives would be preparing hams and geese.

Four hundred miles ahead of me the story would be the same, the carols in my own language but many of the tunes the same, and it would be turkey instead of goose. But whether you call it *Weihnacht* or Christmas, it's the same all over the Christian world, and it was good to be going home.

From Lakenheath I knew I could get a lift down to London in the liberty bus, leaving just after midnight; from London I was confident I could hitch a lift to my parents' home in Kent. By breakfast time I'd be celebrating with my own family. The altimeter read 27,000 feet. I eased the nose forward, reduced throttle setting to give me an air speed of 485 knots and held her steady on 265 degrees. Somewhere beneath me in the gloom the Dutch border would be slipping away, and I had been airborne for twenty-one minutes. No problem.

The problem started ten minutes out over the North Sea, and it started so quietly that it was several minutes before I realized I had one at all. For some time I had been unaware that the low hum coming through my headphones into my ears had ceased, to be replaced by the strange nothingness of total silence. I must have been failing to concentrate, my thoughts being of home and my waiting family. The first thing I knew was when I flicked a glance downward to check my course on the compass. Instead of being rock-steady on 265 degrees, the needle was drifting lazily round the clock, passing through east, west, south, and north with total impartiality.

I swore a most unseasonal sentiment against the compass and the instrument fitter who should have checked it for 100-percent reliability. Compass failure at night, even a brilliant moonlit night such as the one beyond the cockpit Perspex, was no fun. Still, it was not too serious: there was a standby compass—the alcohol kind. But, when I glanced at it, that one seemed to be in trouble, too. The needle was swinging wildly. Apparently something had jarred the case—which isn't uncommon. In any event, I could call up Lakenheath in a few minutes and they would give me a GCA—Ground Controlled Approach—the second-by-second instructions that a well-equipped airfield can give a pilot to bring him home in the worst of weathers, following his progress on ultraprecise radar screens, watching him descend all the way to the tarmac, tracing his position in the sky yard by yard and second by second. I glanced at my watch: thirty-four minutes airborne. I could try to raise Lakenheath now, at the outside limit of my radio range.

Before trying Lakenheath, the correct procedure would be to inform Channel D, to which I was tuned, of my little problem, so they could advise Lakenheath that I was on my way without a compass. I pressed the TRANSMIT button and called:

"Celle, Charlie Delta, Celle, Charlie Delta, calling North Beveland Control...."

I stopped. There was no point in going on. Instead of the lively crackle of static and the sharp sound of my own voice coming back into my own ears, there was a muffled murmur inside my oxygen mask. My own voice speaking...and going nowhere. I tried again. Same result. Far back across the wastes of the black and bitter North Sea, in the warm, cheery concrete complex of North Beveland Control, men sat back from their control panel, chatting and sipping their steaming coffee and cocoa. And they could not hear me. The radio was dead.

Fighting down the rising sense of panic that can kill a pilot faster than anything else, I swallowed and slowly counted to ten. Then I switched to Channel F and tried to raise Lakenheath, ahead of me amid the Suffolk countryside, lying in its forest of pine trees south of Thetford, beautifully equipped with its GCA system for bringing home lost aircraft. On Channel F the radio was as dead as ever. My own muttering into the oxygen mask was smothered by the surrounding rubber. The steady whistle of my own jet engine behind me was my only answer.

It's a very lonely place, the sky, and even more so the sky on a winter's night. And a single-seater jet fighter is a lonely home, a tiny steel box held aloft on stubby wings, hurled through the freezing emptiness by a blazing tube throwing out the strength of six thousand horses every second. But the loneliness is offset, canceled out, by the knowledge that at the touch of a button on the throttle, the pilot can talk to other human beings, people who care about him, men and women who staff a network of stations around the world; just one touch of that button, the

TRANSMIT button, and scores of them in control towers across the land that are tuned to his channel can hear him call for help. When the pilot transmits, on every one of those screens a line of light streaks from the center of the screen to the outside rim, which is marked with figures, from one to three hundred and sixty. Where the streak of light hits the ring, that is where the aircraft lies in relation to the control tower listening to him. The control towers are linked, so with two cross bearings they can locate his position to within a few hundred yards. He is not lost any more. People begin working to bring him down.

The radar operators pick up the little dot he makes on their screens from all the other dots; they call him up and give him instructions. "Begin your descent now, Charlie Delta. We have you now...." Warm, experienced voices, voices which control an array of electronic devices that can reach out across the winter sky, through the ice and rain, above the snow and cloud, to pluck the lost one from his deadly infinity and bring him down to the flare-lit runway that means home and life itself.

When the pilot transmits. But for that he must have a radio. Before I had finished testing Channel J, the international emergency channel, and obtained the same negative result, I knew my ten-channel radio set was as dead as the dodo.

It had taken the RAF two years to train me to fly their fighters for them, and most of that time had been spent in training precisely for emergency procedures. The important thing, they used to say in flying school, is not to know how to fly in perfect conditions; it is to fly through an emergency and stay alive. Now the training was beginning to take effect.

While I was vainly testing my radio channels, my eyes scanned the instrument panel in front of me. The instruments told their own message. It was no coincidence the compass and the radio had failed together; both worked off the aircraft's electrical circuits. Somewhere beneath my feet, amid the miles of brightly colored wiring that make up the circuits, there had been a main fuse blowout. I reminded myself, idiotically, to forgive the instrument fitter and blame the electrician. Then I took stock of the nature of my disaster.

The first thing to do in such a case, I remembered old Flight Sergeant Norris telling us, is to reduce throttle setting from cruise speed to a slower setting, to give maximum flight endurance.

"We don't want to waste valuable fuel, do we, gentlemen? We might need it later. So we reduce the power setting from 10,000 revolutions per minute to 7,200. That way we will fly a little slower, but we will stay in the air rather longer, won't we, gentlemen?" He always referred to us all being in the same emergency at the same time, did Sergeant Norris. I eased the throttle back and watched the rev counter. It operates on its own generator and so I hadn't lost that, at least. I waited until the Goblin was turning over at about 7,200 rpm, and felt the aircraft slow down. The nose rose fractionally, so I adjusted the flight trim to keep her straight and level.

The main instruments in front of a pilot's eyes are six, including the compass. The five others are the air-speed indicator, the altimeter, the vertical-speed indicator, the bank indicator (which tells him if he's banking, i.e., turning, to left or right), and the slip indicator (which tells him if he's skidding crabwise across the sky). Two of these are electrically operated, and they had gone the same way as my compass. That left me with the three pressure-operated instruments—air-speed indicator, altimeter and vertical-speed indicator. In other words, I knew how fast I was going, how high I was and if I were diving or climbing.

It is perfectly possible to land an aircraft with only these three instruments, judging the rest by those old navigational aids, the human eyes. Possible, that is, in conditions of brilliant weather, by daylight and with no cloud in the sky. It is possible, just possible, though not advisable, to try to navigate a fast-moving jet by dead reckoning, using the eyes, looking down and identifying the curve of the coast where it makes an easily recognizable pattern, spotting a strange-shaped reservoir, the glint of a river that the map strapped to the thigh says can only be the Ouse, or the Trent, or the Thames. From lower down it is possible to differentiate Norwich Cathedral tower from Lincoln Cathedral tower, if you know the countryside intimately. By night it is not possible.

The only things that show up at night, even on a bright moonlit night, are the lights. These have patterns when seen from the sky. Manchester looks different from Birmingham;

Southampton can be recognized from the shape of its massive harbor and the Solent, cut out in black (the sea shows up black) against the carpet of the city's lights. I knew Norwich very well, and if I could identify the great curving bulge of the Norfolk coast line from Lowestoft, round through Yarmouth to Cromer, I could find Norwich, the only major sprawl of lights set twenty miles inland from all points on the coast. Five miles north of Norwich, I knew, was the fighter airfield of Merriam St. George, whose red indicator beacon would be blipping out its Morse identification signal into the night. There, if they only had the sense to switch on the airfield lights when they heard me screaming at low level up and down the airfield, I could land safely.

I began to let the Vampire down slowly toward the oncoming coast, my mind feverishly working out how far behind schedule I was through the reduced speed. My watch told me forty-three minutes airborne. The coast of Norfolk had to be somewhere ahead of my nose, five miles below. I glanced up at the full moon, like a searchlight in the glittering sky, and thanked her for her presence.

As the fighter slipped toward Norfolk the sense of loneliness gripped me tighter and tighter. All those things that had seemed so beautiful as I climbed away from the airfield in Lower Saxony now seemed my worst enemies. The stars were no longer impressive in their brilliance; I thought of their hostility, sparkling away there in the timeless, lost infinities of endless space. The night sky, its stratospheric temperature fixed, night and day alike, at an unchanging fifty-six degrees below zero, became in my mind a limitless prison creaking with the cold. Below me lay the worst of them all, the heavy brutality of the North Sea, waiting to swallow up me and my plane and bury us for endless eternity in a liquid black crypt where nothing moved nor would ever move again. And no one would ever know.

At 15,000 feet and still diving, I began to realize that a fresh, and for me the last, enemy had entered the field. There was no ink-black sea three miles below me, no necklace of twinkling seaside lights somewhere up ahead. Far away, to right and left, ahead and no doubt behind me, the light of the moon reflected on a flat and endless sea of white. Perhaps only a hundred, two hundred feet thick, but enough. Enough to blot out all vision, enough to kill me. The East Anglian fog had moved in.

As I had flown westward from Germany, a slight breeze, unforeseen by the weathermen, had sprung up, blowing from the North Sea toward Norfolk. During the previous day the flat, open ground of East Anglia had been frozen hard by the wind and the subzero temperatures. During the evening the wind had moved a belt of slightly warmer air off the North Sea and onto the plains of East Anglia.

There, coming in contact with the ice-cold earth, the trillions of tiny moisture particles in the sea air had vaporized, forming the kind of fog that can blot out five counties in a matter of thirty minutes. How far westward it stretched I could not tell; to the West Midlands, perhaps, nudging up against the eastern slopes of the Pennines? There was no question of trying to overfly the fog to the westward; without navigational aids or radio, I would be lost over strange, unfamiliar country. Also out of the question was to try to fly back to Holland, to land at one of the Dutch Air Force bases along the coast there; I had not the fuel. Relying only on my eyes to guide me, it was a question of landing at Merriam St. George or dying amid the wreckage of the Vampire somewhere in the fog-wreathed fens of Norfolk.

At 10,000 feet I pulled out of my dive, increasing power slightly to keep myself airborne, using up more of my precious fuel. Still a creature of my training, I recalled again the instructions of Flight Sergeant Norris:

"When we are totally lost above unbroken cloud, gentlemen, we must consider the necessity of bailing out of our aircraft, must we not?"

Of course, Sergeant. Unfortunately, the Martin Baker ejector seat cannot be fitted to the single-seat Vampire, which is notorious for being almost impossible to bail out of; the only two successful candidates living lost their legs in the process. Still, there has to be a lucky one. What else, Sergeant?

"Our first move, therefore, is to turn our aircraft toward the open sea, away from all areas of intense human habitation."

You mean towns, Sergeant. Those people down there pay for us to fly for them, not to drop a screaming monster of ten tons of steel on top of them on Christmas Eve. There are kids down there, schools, hospitals, homes. You turn your aircraft out to sea.

The procedures were all worked out. They did not mention that the chances of a pilot, bobbing about on a winter's night in the North Sea, frozen face lashed by a subzero wind, supported by a yellow life jacket, ice encrusting his lips, eyebrows, ears, his position unknown by the men sipping their Christmas punches in warm rooms three hundred miles away—that his chances were less than one in a hundred of living longer than one hour. In the training films, they showed you pictures of happy fellows who had announced by radio that they were ditching, being picked up by helicopters within minutes, and all on a bright, warm summer's day.

"One last procedure, gentlemen, to be used in extreme emergency."

That's better, Sergeant Norris, that's what I'm in now.

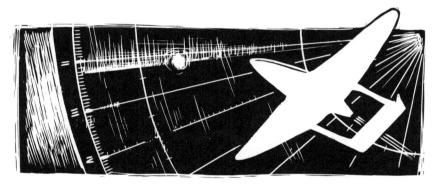

"All haircraft happroaching Britain's coasts are visible on the radar screens of our early-warning system. If, therefore, we have lost our radio and cannot transmit our emergency, we try to attract the attention of our radar scanners by adopting an odd form of behavior. We do this by moving out to sea, then flying in small triangles, turning left, left and left again, each leg of the triangle being of a duration of two minutes' flying time. In this way we hope to attract attention. When we have been spotted, the air-traffic controller is informed and he diverts another aircraft to find us. This other aircraft, of course, has a radio. When discovered by the rescue aircraft, we formate on him and he brings us down through the cloud or fog to a safe landing."

Yes, it was the last attempt to save one's life. I recalled the details better now. The rescue aircraft which would lead you back to a safe landing, flying wing tip to wing tip, was called the shepherd. I glanced at my watch; fifty-one minutes airborne, about thirty minutes left of fuel. Then I looked at the fuel gauge and saw that I'd lost it along with the rest when the fuse blew. I had an icy moment until I remembered the worry button—which I could press to get an approximate reading. The fuel gauge read one-third full. Knowing myself to be still short of the Norfolk coast, and flying level at 10,000 feet in the moonlight, I pulled the Vampire into a left-hand turn and began my first leg of the first triangle. After two minutes, I pulled left again. Below me, the fog reached back as far as I could see, and ahead of me, toward Norfolk, it was the same.

Ten minutes went by, nearly two complete triangles. I had not prayed, not really prayed, for many years, and the habit came hard. Lord, please get me out of this bloody mess.... No, you mustn't talk like that to Him. "Our Father, which art in Heaven..." He'd heard that a thousand times, would be hearing it another thousand times tonight. What do you say to Him when you want help? Please, God, make somebody notice me up here; please make someone see me flying in triangles and send up a shepherd to help me down to a safe landing. Please help me, and I promise—What on earth could I promise Him? He had no need of me, and I, who now had need of Him, had taken no notice of Him for so long He'd probably forgotten all about me.

When I had been airborne for seventy-two minutes, I knew no one would come. The compass still drifted aimlessly through all the points of the circle, the other electrical instruments were dead, all their needles frozen at the point where they'd stopped. My altimeter read 7,000 feet, so I had dropped 3,000 feet while turning. No matter. The fuel read between zero and a quarter full—say ten minutes' more flying time. I felt the rage of despair welling up. I began screaming into the dead microphone:

"You stupid bastards, why don't you look at your radar screens? Why can't somebody see me up here? All so damn drunk you can't do your jobs properly. Oh, God, why won't somebody listen to me?" By then the anger had subsided and I had taken to blubbering like a baby from the sheer helplessness of it all.

Five minutes later, I knew, without any doubt of it, that I was going to die that night. Strangely I wasn't even afraid any more. Just enormously sad. Sad for all the things I would never do, the places I would never see, the people I would never greet again. It's a bad thing, a sad thing, to die at twenty years of age with your life unlived, and the worst thing of all is not the fact of dying but the fact of all the things never done.

Out through the Perspex I could see that the moon was setting, hovering above the horizon of thick white fog; in another two minutes the night sky would be plunged into total darkness and a few minutes later, I would have to bail out of a dying aircraft before it flicked over on its last dive into the North Sea. An hour later I would be dead also, bobbing around in the water, a bright-yellow Mae West supporting a stiff, frozen body. I dropped the left wing of the Vampire toward the moon to bring the aircraft onto the final leg of the last triangle.

Down below the wing tip, against the sheen of the fog bank, up-moon of me, a black shadow crossed the whiteness. For a second I thought it was my own shadow, but with the moon up there, my own shadow would be behind me. It was another aircraft, low against the fog bank, keeping station with me through my turn, a mile down through the sky toward the fog.

The other aircraft being below me, I kept turning, wing down, to keep it in sight. The other aircraft also kept turning, until the two of us had done one complete circle. Only then did I realize why it was so far below me, why he did not climb to my height and take up station on my wing tip. He was flying slower than I; he could not keep up if he tried to fly beside me. Trying hard not to believe he was just another aircraft, moving on his way, about to disappear forever into the fog bank, I eased the throttle back and began to slip down toward him. He kept turning; so did I. At 5,000 feet I knew I was still going too fast for him. I could not reduce power any more for fear of stalling the Vampire and plunging down out of control. To slow up even more, I put out the air brakes. The Vampire shuddered as the brakes swung into the slipstream, slowing the Vampire down to 280 knots.

And then he came up toward me, swinging in toward my left-hand wing tip. I could make out the black bulk of him against the dim white sheet of fog below; then he was with me, a hundred feet off my wing tip, and we straightened out together, rocking as we tried to keep formation. The moon was to my right, and my own shadow masked his shape and form; but even so, I could make out the shimmer of two propellers whirling through the sky ahead of him. Of course, he could not fly at my speed; I was in a jet fighter, he in a piston-engined aircraft of an earlier generation.

He held station alongside me for a few seconds, down-moon of me, half invisible, then banked gently to the left. I followed, keeping formation with him, for he was obviously the shepherd sent up to bring me down, and he had the compass and the radio, not I. He swung through 180 degrees, then straightened up, flying straight and level, the moon behind him. From the position of the dying moon I knew we were heading back toward the Norfolk coast, and for the first time I could see him well. To my surprise, my shepherd was a De Havilland Mosquito, a fighter bomber of Second World War vintage.

Then I remembered that the Meteorological Squadron at Gloucester used Mosquitoes, the last ones flying, to take samples of the upper atmosphere to help in the preparation of weather forecasts. I had seen them at Battle of Britain displays, flying their Mosquitoes in the flypasts, attracting gasps from the crowd and a few nostalgic shakes of the head from the older men, such as they always reserved on September 15 for the Spitfires, Hurricanes and Lancasters.

Inside the cockpit of the Mosquito I could make out, against the light of the moon, the muffled head of its pilot and the twin circles of his goggles as he looked out the side window toward me. Carefully, he raised his right hand till I could see it in the window, fingers straight, palm downward. He jabbed the fingers forward and down, meaning, "We are going to descend; formate on me."

I nodded and quickly brought up my own left hand so he could see it, pointing forward to my own control panel with one forefinger, then holding up five splayed fingers. Finally, I drew my hand across my throat. By common agreement this sign means I have only five minutes' fuel left, then my engine cuts out. I saw the muffled, goggled, oxygen-masked head nod in understanding, then we were heading downward toward the sheet of fog. His speed increased and I brought the air brakes back in. The Vampire stopped trembling and plunged ahead of the Mosquito. I pulled back on the throttle, hearing the engine die to a low whistle, and the shepherd was back beside me. We were diving straight toward the shrouded land of Norfolk. I glanced at my altimeter: 2,000 feet, still diving.

He pulled out at three hundred feet; the fog was still below us. Probably the fog bank was only from the ground to one hundred feet up, but that was more than enough to prevent a plane from landing without a GCA. I could imagine the stream of instructions coming from the radar hut into the earphones of the man flying beside me, eighty feet away through two panes of Perspex and the windstream of icy air moving between us at 280 knots. I kept my eyes on him, formating as closely as possible, afraid of losing sight for an instant, watching for his every hand signal. Against the white fog, even as the moon sank, I had to marvel at the beauty of his aircraft; the short nose and bubble cockpit, the blister of Perspex right in the nose itself, the long, lean, underslung engine pods, each housing a Rolls-Royce Merlin engine, a masterpiece of craftsmanship, snarling through the night toward home. Two minutes later he held up his clenched left fist in the window, then opened the fist to splay all five fingers against the glass. "Please lower your undercarriage." I moved the lever downward and felt the dull thunk as all three wheels went down, happily powered by hydraulic pressure and not dependent on the failed electrical system.

The pilot of the shepherd aircraft pointed down again, for another descent, and as he jinked in the moonlight I caught sight of the nose of the Mosquito. It had the letters JK painted on it, large and black. Probably for call sign Jig King. Then we were descending again, more gently this time.

He leveled out just above the fog layer, so low the tendrils of candy floss were lashing at our fuselages, and we went into a steady circular turn. I managed to flick a glance at my fuel gauge; it was on zero, flickering feebly. For God's sake, hurry up, I prayed, for if my fuel failed me now, there would be no time to climb to the minimum seven hundred feet needed for bailing out. A jet fighter at one hundred feet without an engine is a death trap with no chance for survival.

For two or three minutes he seemed content to hold his slow circular turn, while the sweat broke out behind my neck and began to run in streams down my back, gumming the light nylon flying suit to my skin. HURRY UP, MAN, HURRY.

Quite suddenly he straightened out, so fast I almost lost him by continuing to turn. I caught him a second later and saw his left hand flash the "dive" signal to me. Then he dipped toward the fog bank; I followed, and we were in it, a shallow, flat descent, but a descent nevertheless, and from a mere hundred feet, toward nothing.

To pass out of even dimly lit sky into cloud or fog is like passing into a bath of gray cotton wool. Suddenly there is nothing but the gray, whirling strands, a million tendrils reaching out to trap and strangle you, each one touching the cockpit cover with a quick caress, then disappearing back into nothingness. The visibility was down to near zero, no shape, no size, no form, no substance. Except that off my left wing tip, now only forty feet away, was the form of a Mosquito flying with absolute certainty toward something I could not see. Only then did I realize he was flying without lights. For a second I was amazed, horrified by my discovery; then I realized the wisdom of the man. Lights in fog are treacherous, hallucinatory, mesmeric. You can get attracted to them, not knowing whether they are forty or a hundred feet away from you. The tendency is to move toward them; for two aircraft in the fog, one flying formation on the other, that could spell disaster. The man was right.

Keeping formation with him, I knew he was slowing down, for I, too, was easing back the throttle, dropping and slowing. In a fraction of a second I flashed a glance at the two instruments I needed; the altimeter was reading zero, so was the fuel gauge, and neither was even flickering. The air-speed indicator, which I had also seen, read 120 knots—and this damn coffin was going to fall out of the sky at 95.

Without warning the shepherd pointed a single forefinger at me, then forward through the windscreen. It meant, "There you are, fly on and land." I stared forward through the now streaming windshield. Nothing. Then, yes, something. A blur to the left, another to the right, then two, one on each side. Ringed with haze, there were lights on either side of me, in pairs, flashing past. I forced my eyes to see what lay between them. Nothing, blackness. Then a streak of paint running under my feet. The center line. Frantically I closed down the power and held her steady, praying for the Vampire to settle.

The lights were rising now, almost at eye level, and still she would not settle. Bang. We touched, we touched the flaming deck. Bang-bang. Another touch, she was drifting again, inches above the wet black runway. Bam-bam-bam-babam-rumble. She was down; the main wheels had stuck and held.

The Vampire was rolling, at over ninety miles an hour, through a sea of gray fog. I touched the brakes and the nose slammed down onto the deck also. Slow pressure now, no skidding, hold her straight against the skid, more pressure on those brakes or we'll run off the end. The lights moving past more leisurely now, slowing, slower, slower....

The Vampire stopped. I found both of my hands clenched round the control column, squeezing the brake lever inward. I forget now how many seconds I held them there before I would believe we were stopped. Finally, I did believe it, put on the parking brake and released the main brake. Then I went to turn off the engine, for there was no use trying to taxi in this fog; they would have to tow the fighter back with a Land-Rover. There was no need to turn off the engine; it had finally run out of fuel as the Vampire careered down the runway. I shut off the remaining systems—fuel, hydraulics, electrics and pressurization—and slowly began to unstrap myself from the seat and parachute/dinghy pack. As I did so, a movement caught my eye. To my left, through the fog, no more than fifty feet away, low on the ground with wheels up, the Mosquito roared past me. I caught the flash of the pilot's hand in the side window, then he was gone, up into the fog, before he could see my answering wave of acknowledgment. But I'd already decided to call up RAF Gloucester and thank him personally from the officers' mess.

With the systems off, the cockpit was misting up fast, so I released the canopy and wound the hood backward by hand

until it locked. Only then, as I stood up, did I realize how cold
it was. Against my heated body, dressed in a light nylon flying
suit, it was freezing. I expected the control tower truck to be
alongside in seconds, for, with an emergency landing, even on
Christmas Eve, the fire truck, ambulance and half a dozen other
vehicles were always standing by. Nothing happened. At least
not for ten minutes.

By the time the two headlights came groping out of the mist, I
felt frozen. The lights stopped twenty feet from the motionless
Vampire, dwarfed by the fighter's bulk. A voice called, "Hallo
there."

I stepped out of the cockpit, jumped from the wing to the
tarmac, and ran toward the lights. They turned out to be the
headlamps of a battered old Jowett Javelin. Not an Air Force
identification mark in sight. At the wheel of the car was a
puffed, beery face and a handlebar moustache. At least he wore
an RAF officer's cap. He stared at me as I loomed out of the fog.

"That yours?" He nodded toward the dim shape of the
Vampire.

"Yes," I said. "I just landed it."

"'Straordinary," he said, "quite 'straordinary. You'd better jump
in. I'll run you back to the mess."

I was grateful for the warmth of the car, even more so to be
alive.

Moving in bottom gear, he began to ease the old car back
round the taxi track, evidently toward the control tower and,
beyond it, the mess buildings. As we moved away from the
Vampire, I saw that I had stopped twenty feet short of a plowed
field at the very end of the runway.

"You were damned lucky," he said, or rather shouted, for the
engine was roaring in first gear and he seemed to be having
trouble with the foot controls. Judging by the smell of whisky
on his breath, that was not surprising.

"Damned lucky," I agreed. "I ran out of fuel just as I was landing. My radio and all the electrical systems failed nearly fifty
minutes ago over the North Sea."

He spent several minutes digesting the information carefully.

"'Straordinary," he said at length. "No compass?"

"No compass. Flying in the approximate direction by the

moon. As far as the coast, or where I judged it to be. After that…"

"No radio?"

"No radio," I said. "A dead box on all channels."

"Then how did you find this place?" he asked.

I was losing patience. The man was evidently one of those passed-over flight lieutenants, not terribly bright and probably not a flier, despite the handlebar moustache. A ground wallah. And drunk with it. Shouldn't be on duty at all on an operational station at that hour of the night.

"I was guided in," I explained patiently. The emergency procedures, having worked so well, now began to seem run-of-the-mill; such is the recuperation of youth. "I flew short, left-hand triangles, as per instructions, and they sent up a shepherd aircraft to guide me down. No problem."

He shrugged, as if to say "If you insist." Finally, he said: "Damned lucky, all the same. I'm surprised the other chap managed to find the place."

"No problem there," I said. "It was one of the weather aircraft from RAF Gloucester. Obviously, he had radio. So we came in here in formation, on a GCA. Then, when I saw the lights at the threshold of the runway, I landed myself."

The man was obviously dense, as well as drunk.

"'Straordinary," he said, sucking a stray drop of moisture off his handlebar. "We don't have GCA. We don't have any navigational equipment at all, not even a beacon."

Now it was my turn to let the information sink in.

"This isn't RAF Merriam St. George?" I asked in a small voice.
He shook his head.

"Marham? Chicksands? Lakenheath?"

"No," he said, "this is RAF Minton."

"I've never heard of it," I said at last.

"I'm not surprised. We're not an operational station. Haven't been for years. Minton's a storage depot. Excuse me."

He stopped the car and got out. I saw we were standing a few feet from the dim shape of a control tower adjoining a long row of Nissen huts, evidently once flight rooms, navigational and briefing huts. Above the narrow door at the base of the tower through which the officer had disappeared hung a single naked bulb. By its light I could make out broken windows, padlocked doors, an air of abandonment and neglect. The man returned and climbed shakily back behind the wheel.

"Just turning the runway lights off," he said, and belched.

My mind was whirling. This was mad, crazy, illogical. Yet there had to be a perfectly reasonable explanation.

"Why did you switch them on?" I asked.

"It was the sound of your engine," he said. "I was in the officers' mess having a noggin, and old Joe suggested I listen out the window for a second. There you were, circling right above us. You sounded damn low, almost as if you were going to come down in a hurry. Thought I might be of some use, remembered they never disconnected the old runway lights when they dismantled the station, so I ran down to the control tower and switched them on."

"I see," I said, but I didn't. But there had to be an explanation.

"That was why I was so late coming out to pick you up. I had to go back to the mess to get the car out, once I'd heard you land out there. Then I had to find you. Bloody foggy night."

You can say that again, I thought. The mystery puzzled me for another few minutes. Then I hit on the explanation.

"Where is RAF Minton, exactly?" I asked him.

"Five miles in from the coast, inland from Cromer. That's where we are," he said.

"And where's the nearest operational RAF station with all the radio aids, including GCA?"

He thought for a minute.

"Must be Merriam St. George," he said. "They must have all those things. Mind you, I'm just a stores johnny."

That was the explanation. My unknown friend in the weather plane had been leading me straight in from the coast to Merriam St. George. By chance, Minton, abandoned old stores depot Minton, with its cobwebbed runway lights and drunken commanding officer, lay right along the in-flight path to Merriam's runway. Merriam's controller had asked us to circle twice while he switched on his runway lights ten miles ahead, and this old fool had switched on his lights as well. Result: Coming in on the last ten-mile stretch, I had plonked my Vampire down onto the wrong airfield. I was about to tell him not to interfere with modern procedures that he couldn't understand when I choked the words back. My fuel had run out halfway down the runway. I'd never have made Merriam, ten miles away. I'd have crashed in the fields short of touchdown. By an amazing fluke I had been, as he said, damned lucky.

By the time I had worked out the rational explanation for my presence at this nearly abandoned airfield, we had reached the officers' mess. My host parked his car in front of the door and we climbed out. Above the entrance hall a light was burning, dispelling the fog and illuminating the carved but chipped crest of the Royal Air Force above the doorway. To one side was a board screwed to the wall. It read RAF STATION MINTON. To the other side was another board, announcing OFFICERS' MESS. We walked inside.

The front hall was large and spacious, but evidently built in the prewar years when metal window frames, service issue, were in fashion. The place reeked of the expression "It has seen better days." It had, indeed. Only two cracked-leather club chairs occupied the anteroom, which could have taken twenty. The cloakroom to the right contained a long empty rail for nonexistent coats. My host, who told me he was Flight Lieutenant Marks, shrugged off his sheepskin coat and threw it over a chair. He was wearing his uniform-trousers but with a chunky blue pullover for a jacket. It must be miserable to spend your Christmas on duty in a dump like this.

He told me he was the second-in-command, the C.O. being a squadron leader now on Christmas leave. Apart from him and his C.O., the station boasted a sergeant, three corporals, one of whom was on Christmas duty and presumably in the corporals' mess also on his own, and twenty stores clerks, all away on leave. When not on leave, they spent their days classifying tons of surplus clothing, parachutes, boots and other impedimenta that go to make up a fighting service.

There was no fire in the vestibule, though there was a large brick fireplace, nor any in the bar, either. Both rooms were freezing cold, and I was beginning to shiver again after recovering in the car. Marks was putting his head through the various doors leading off the hall, shouting for someone called Joe. By looking through after him, I took in at a glance the spacious but deserted dining room, also fireless and cold, and the twin passages, one leading to the officers' private rooms, the other to the staff quarters. RAF messes do not vary much in architecture; once a pattern, always a pattern.

"I'm sorry it's not very hospitable, old boy," said Marks, having failed to find the absent Joe. "Being only the two of us on station here, and no visitors to speak of, we've each made two bedrooms into a sort of self-contained apartment where we live. Hardly seems worth using all this space just for the two of us. You can't heat it in winter, you know; not on the fuel they allow us. And you can't get the staff."

It seemed sensible. In his position, I'd probably have done the same.

"Not to worry," I said, dropping my flying helmet and attached oxygen mask onto the other leather chair in the anteroom. "Though I could do with a bath and a meal."

"I think we can manage that," he said, trying hard to play the genial host. "I'll get Joe to fix up one of the spare rooms—God knows we have enough of them—and heat up the water. He'll also rustle up a meal. Not much, I'm afraid. Bacon and eggs do?"

I nodded. By this time I presumed old Joe was the mess steward.

"That will do fine. While I'm waiting, do you mind if I use your phone?"

"Certainly, certainly, of course, you'll have to check in."

He ushered me into the mess secretary's office, through a door beside the entrance to the bar. It was small and cold, but it had a chair, an empty desk and a telephone. I dialed 100 for the local operator and while I was waiting, Marks returned with a tumbler of whisky. Normally, I hardly touch spirits, but it was warming, so I thanked him and he went off to supervise the steward. My watch told me it was close to midnight. Hell of a way to spend Christmas, I thought. Then I recalled how, thirty minutes earlier, I had been crying to God for a bit of help, and felt ashamed.

"Little Minton," said a drowsy voice. It took ages to get through, for I had no telephone number for Merriam St. George, but the girl got it eventually. Down the line I could hear the telephone operator's family celebrating in a back room, no doubt the living quarters attached to the village post office. After a few minutes, the phone was ringing.

"RAF Merriam St. George," said a man's voice. Duty sergeant speaking from the guardroom, I thought.

"Duty Controller, Air-Traffic Control, please," I said. There was a pause.

"I'm sorry, sir," said the voice, "may I ask who's calling?"

I gave him my name and rank. Speaking from RAF Minton, I told him.

"I see, sir. But I'm afraid there's no flying tonight, sir. No one on duty in Air-Traffic Control. A few of the officers up in the mess, though."

"Then give me the Station Duty Officer, please."

When I got through to him, he was evidently in the mess, for the sound of lively talk could be heard behind him. I explained about the emergency and the fact that his station had been alerted to receive a Vampire fighter coming in on an emergency GCA without radio. He listened attentively. Perhaps he was young and conscientious, too, for he was quite sober, as a station duty officer is supposed to be at all times, even Christmas.

"I don't know about that," he said at length. "I don't think we've been operational since we closed down at five this afternoon. But I'm not on Air-Traffic. Would you hold on? I'll get the wing commander—flying. He's here."

There was a pause and then an older voice came on the line.

"Where are you speaking from?" he said, after noting my name, rank and the station at which I was based.

"RAF Minton, sir. I've just made an emergency landing here. Apparently, it's nearly abandoned."

"Yes, I know," he drawled. "Damn bad luck. Do you want us to send a Tilly for you?"

"No, it's not that, sir. I don't mind being here. It's just that I landed at the wrong airfield. I believe I was heading for your airfield on a ground-controlled approach."

"Well, make up your mind. Were you or weren't you? You ought to know. According to what you say, you were flying the damn thing."

I took a deep breath and started at the beginning.

"So you see, sir, I was intercepted by the weather plane from Gloucester and he brought me in. But in this fog it must have been on a GCA. No other way to get down. Yet when I saw the lights of Minton, I landed here, assuming it to be Merriam St. George."

"Splendid," he said at length. "Marvelous bit of flying by that pilot from Gloucester. 'Course, those chaps are up in all weathers. It's their job. What do you want us to do about it?"

I was getting exasperated. Wing commander he might have been, but he had had a skinful this Christmas Eve.

"I am ringing to alert you to stand down your radar and traffic-control crews, sir. They must be waiting for a Vampire that's never going to arrive. It's already arrived—here at Minton."

"But we're closed down," he said. "We shut all the systems down at five o'clock. There's been no call for us to turn out."

"But Merriam St. George has a GCA," I protested.

"I know we have," he shouted back. "But it hasn't been used tonight. It's been shut down since five o'clock."

I asked the next and last question slowly and carefully.

"Do you know, sir, where is the nearest RAF station that will be manning one-twenty-one-point-five-megacycle band throughout the night, the nearest station to here that maintains twenty-four-hour emergency listening?" The international aircraft-emergency frequency is 121.5 megacycles.

"Yes," he said equally slowly. "To the west, RAF Marham. To the south, RAF Lakenheath. Good night to you. Happy Christmas."

I put the phone down and sat back and breathed deeply.

Marham was forty miles away on the other side of Norfolk. Lakenheath was forty miles to the south, in Suffolk. On the fuel I was carrying, not only could I not have made Merriam St. George, it wasn't even open. So how could I ever have got to Marham or Lakenheath? And I had told that Mosquito pilot that I had only five minutes' fuel left. He had acknowledged that he understood. In any case, he was flying far too low after we dived into the fog ever to fly forty miles like that. The man must have been mad.

It began to dawn on me that I didn't really owe my life to the weather pilot from Gloucester, but to Flight Lieutenant Marks, beery, bumbling old passed-over Flight Lieutenant Marks, who couldn't tell one end of an aircraft from another but who had run four hundred yards through the fog to switch on the lights of an abandoned runway because he heard a jet engine circling overhead too close to the ground. Still, the Mosquito must be back at Gloucester by now and he ought to know that, despite everything, I was alive.

"Gloucester?" said the operator. "At this time of night?"

"Yes," I replied firmly, "Gloucester, at this time of night."

One thing about weather squadrons, they're always on duty. The duty meteorologist took the call. I explained the position to him.

"I'm afraid there must be some mistake, Flying Officer," he said. "It could not have been one of ours."

"This *is* RAF Gloucester, right?"

"Yes, it is. Duty Officer speaking."

"Fine. And your unit flies Mosquitoes to take pressure and temperature readings at altitude, right?"

"Wrong," he said. "We used to use Mosquitoes. They went out of service three months ago. We now use Canberras."

I sat holding the telephone, staring at it in disbelief. Then an idea came to me.

"What happened to them?" I asked. He must have been an elderly boffin of great courtesy and patience to tolerate darn-fool questions at that hour.

"They were scrapped, I think, or sent off to museums, more likely. They're getting quite rare nowadays, you know."

"I know," I said. "Could one of them have been sold privately?"

"I suppose it's possible," he said at length. "It would depend on Air Ministry policy. But I think they went to aircraft museums."

"Thank you. Thank you very much. And Happy Christmas."

I put the phone down and shook my head in bewilderment. What a night, what an incredible night! First I lose my radio and all my instruments, then I get lost and short of fuel, then I am taken in tow by some moonlighting harebrain with a passion for veteran aircraft flying his own Mosquito through the night, who happens to spot me, comes within an inch of killing me, and finally a half-drunk ground-duty officer has the sense to put his runway lights on in time to save me. Luck doesn't come in much bigger slices. But one thing was certain; that amateur air ace hadn't the faintest idea what he was doing. On the other hand, where would I be without him? I asked myself. Bobbing around dead in the North Sea by now.

I raised the last of the whisky to him and his strange passion for flying privately in outdated aircraft and tossed the drink down. Flight Lieutenant Marks put his head through the doorway.

"Your room's ready," he said. "Number seventeen, just down the corridor. Joe's making up a fire for you. The bath water's heating. If you don't mind, I think I'll turn in. Will you be all right on your own?"

I greeted him with more friendliness than last time, which he deserved.

"Sure, I'll be fine. Many thanks for all your help."

I took my helmet and wandered down the corridor, flanked with the numbers of the bedrooms of bachelor officers long since posted elsewhere. From the doorway of seventeen, a bar of light shone out into the passage. As I entered the room an old man rose from his knees in front of the fireplace. He gave me a start. Mess stewards are usually RAF enlisted men. This one was near seventy and obviously a locally recruited civilian employee.

"Good evening, sir," he said. "I'm Joe, sir. I'm the mess steward."

"Yes, Joe, Mr. Marks told me about you. Sorry to cause you so much trouble at this hour of the night. I just dropped in, as you might say."

"Yes, Mr. Marks told me. I'll have your room ready directly. Soon as this fire burns up, it'll be quite cozy."

The chill had not been taken off the room and I shivered in the nylon flying suit. I should have asked Marks for the loan of a sweater but had forgotten.

I elected to take my lonely evening meal in my room, and while Joe went to fetch it, I had a quick bath, for the water was by then reasonably hot. While I toweled myself down and wrapped round me the old but warm dressing gown that old Joe had brought with him, he set out a small table and placed a plate of sizzling bacon and eggs on it. By then the room was comfortably warm, the coal fire burning brightly, the curtains drawn. While I ate, which took only a few minutes, for I was ravenously hungry, the old steward stayed to talk.

"You been here long, Joe?" I asked him, more out of politeness than genuine curiosity.

"Oh, yes, sir, nigh on twenty years; since just before the war, when the station opened."

"You've seen some changes, eh? Wasn't always like this."

"That it wasn't, sir, that it wasn't." And he told me of the days when the rooms were crammed with eager young pilots, the dining room noisy with the clatter of plates and cutlery, the bar roaring with bawdy songs; of months and years when the sky above the airfield crackled and snarled to the sound of piston engines driving planes to war and bringing them back again.

While he talked I emptied the remainder of the half-bottle of red wine he had brought from the bar store. A very good steward was Joe. After finishing, I rose from the table, fished a cigarette from the pocket of my flying suit, lit it and sauntered round the room. The steward began to tidy up the plates and the glass from the table. I halted before an old photograph in a frame standing alone on the mantel above the crackling fire. I stopped with my cigarette half-raised to my lips, feeling the room go suddenly cold.

The photo was old and stained, but behind its glass it was still clear enough. It showed a young man of about my own years, in his early twenties, dressed in flying gear. But not the gray suits and gleaming plastic crash helmet of today. He wore thick sheepskin-lined boots, rough serge trousers and a heavy zip-up jacket. From his left hand dangled one of the soft-leather flying helmets they used to wear, with goggles attached, instead of the modern pilot's tinted visor. He stood with legs apart, right hand on hip, a defiant stance, but he was not smiling. He stared at the camera with grim intensity. There was something sad about the eyes.

Behind him, quite clearly visible, stood his aircraft. There was no mistaking the lean, sleek silhouette of the Mosquito fighter-bomber, nor the two low-slung pods housing the twin Merlin engines that gave it its remarkable performance. I was about to say something to Joe when I felt the gust of cold air on my back. One of the windows had blown open and the icy air was rushing in.

"I'll close it, sir," the old man said, and made to put all the plates back down again.

"No, I'll do it."

It took me two strides to cross to where the window swung on its steel frame. To get a better hold, I stepped inside the curtain and stared out. The fog swirled in waves round the old mess building, disturbed by the current of warm air coming from the window. Somewhere, far away in the fog, I thought I heard the snarl of engines. There were no engines out there, just a motorcycle of some farm boy, taking leave of his sweetheart across the fens. I closed the window, made sure it was secure and turned back into the room.

"Who's the pilot, Joe?"

"The pilot, sir?"

I nodded toward the lonely photograph on the mantel.

"Oh, I see, sir. That's a photo of Mr. John Kavanagh. He was here during the war, sir."

He placed the wineglass on top of the topmost plate.

"Kavanagh?" I walked back to the picture and studied it closely.

"Yes, sir. An Irish gentleman. A very fine man, if I may say so. As a matter of fact, sir, this was his room."

"What squadron was that, Joe?" I was still peering at the aircraft in the background.

"Pathfinders, sir. Mosquitoes, they flew. Very fine pilots, all of them, sir. But I venture to say I believe Mr. Johnny was the best of them all. But then I'm biased, sir. I was his batman, you see."

There was no doubting it. The faint letters on the nose of the Mosquito behind the figure in the photo read JK. Not Jig King, but Johnny Kavanagh.

The whole thing was clear as day. Kavanagh had been a fine pilot, flying with one of the crack squadrons during the war. After the war he'd left the Air Force, probably going into second-hand car dealing, as quite a few did. So he'd made a pile of money in the booming Fifties, probably bought himself a fine country house, and had enough left over to indulge his real passion—flying. Or rather re-creating the past, his days of glory. He'd bought up an old Mosquito in one of the RAF periodic auctions of obsolescent aircraft, refitted it and flew it privately whenever he wished. Not a bad way to spend your spare time, if you had the money.

So he'd been flying back from some trip to Europe, had spotted me turning in triangles above the cloud bank, realized I was stuck and taken me in tow. Pinpointing his position precisely by crossed radio beacons, knowing this stretch of the coast by heart, he'd taken a chance on finding his old airfield at Minton, even in thick fog. It was a hell of a risk. But then I had no fuel left, anyway, so it was that or bust.

I had no doubt I could trace the man, probably through the Royal Aero club.

"He was certainly a good pilot," I said reflectively, thinking of this evening's performance.

"The best, sir," said old Joe from behind me. "They reckoned he had eyes like a cat, did Mr. Johnny. I remember many's the time the squadron would return from dropping marker flares over bombing targets in Germany and the rest of the young gentlemen would go into the bar and have a drink. More likely several."

"He didn't drink?" I asked.

"Oh, yes, sir, but more often he'd have his Mosquito refueled and take off again alone, going back over the Channel or the North Sea to see if he could find some crippled bomber making for the coast and guide it home."

I frowned. Those big bombers had their own bases to go to.

"But some of them would have taken a lot of enemy flak fire and sometimes they had their radios knocked out. All over, they came from. Marham, Scampton, Waddington; the big four-engined ones, Halifaxes, Stirlings, and Lancasters; a bit before your time, if you'll pardon my saying so, sir."

"I've seen pictures of them," I admitted. "And some of them fly in air parades. And he used to guide them back?"

I could imagine them in my mind's eye, gaping holes in the body, wings, and tail, creaking and swaying as the pilot sought to hold them steady for home, a wounded or dying crew and the radio shot to bits. And I knew, from too recent experience, the bitter loneliness of the winter's sky at night, with no radio, no guide for home, and the fog blotting out the land.

"That's right, sir. He used to go up for a second flight in the same night, patrolling out over the North Sea, looking for a crippled plane. Then he'd guide it home, back here to Minton, sometimes through fog so dense you couldn't see your hand. Sixth sense, they said he had—something of the Irish in him."

I turned from the photograph and stubbed my cigarette butt into the ashtray by the bed. Joe was at the door.

"Quite a man," I said, and I meant it. Even today, middle-aged, he was a superb flier.

"Oh, yes, sir, quite a man, Mr. Johnny. I remember him saying to me once, standing right where you are, before the fire: 'Joe,' he said, 'whenever there's one of them out there in the night, trying to get back, I'll go out and bring him home.'"

I nodded gravely. The old man so obviously worshiped his wartime officer.

"Well," I said, "by the look of it, he's still doing it."

Now Joe smiled.

"Oh, I hardly think so, sir. Mr. Johnny went out on his last patrol Christmas Eve 1943, just fourteen years ago tonight. He never came back, sir. He went down with his plane somewhere out there in the North Sea. Good night, sir. And Happy Christmas."

The
Cottager's
Dinner

by
PATRICK BRONTË

This single stanza has been extracted from "The Happy Cottagers" by Patrick Brontë, the father of Emily, Anne and Charlotte. Just a simple thought fitting to a Christmas fare.

The Cottager's Dinner

The tablecloth, though coarse,
    Was of a snowy white,
The vessels, spoons, and knives
    Were clean and dazzling bright;
        So down we sat
                Devoid of care,
            Nor envied kings
                Their dainty fare.

The
Lovely
Messengers

by
LAURENCE HOUSMAN
(1865–1959)

The more I read of Laurence Housman, the more convinced I am that he has been most unfairly neglected. "The Lovely Messengers" is one of the loveliest of all Christmas stories. There is a delicacy and lightness of touch in Housman's writing that is positively otherworldly…

I t was Christmas Eve, and the door at the farm was shut to keep out the cold. A woman crept into the porch, and knocked timidly, then for a while waited.

While waiting, she leaned face and hands against one of the side-posts; and from head to foot a slow trembling took hold of her, of cold, and fear, and weakness.

After the third knock a bar was let down from within, and the door swung wide on its hinges; warm light streamed out, show-ing the figure of the supplicant. "Let me in, or I shall die!" the poor thing said, with a heavy forward leaning.

"Who are you?" asked the farm-woman, who had the door in her hand. "Ah, it's *you*!" There was recognition in the tone but not welcome.

"Who is it?" called out the farmer from the ingle-corner. "Don't keep the door agape, letting in all the cold!"

"'Tis Molly, the bad wench," answered the woman; "and she's big; to her shame be it said. Her time is not far off!"

"I won't have her here!" cried the farmer. "Let her carry her shame away from honest folks' doors! Shut it—you there, I say!"

The door was shut-to again, and barred. Molly turned and crept meekly away through the barton, past the cow-pens and outhouses. Presently she stopped, with deep shudderings from head to foot, and leaned against a stack of hurdles for support.

"I can't go on!" she whispered. "I shall die!"

Within wooden walls she heard a rustle of straw and the snored breathings of live stock.

"I shall die, I shall die!" she moaned.

Her hand fell on a wooden bolt, shot home loosely into its socket: at a weak push it yielded, and the door creaked inwards. She entered to a warm vapourish atmosphere of animals and fermenting litter. In a corner where the straw seemed freshest and cleanest she lay down, and felt comparative peace for a while take hold of her wrenched body.

Close by went a slow munching, where the steer and the ass's colt stood loosely stalled side by side. As they munched the extra portion given them for that night's meal, they talked together of the Feast which Heaven and Earth were even then beginning to hold.

"This is the night of our inheritance," said the steer; "our fathers have told us, as their fathers told them; so it has come down to us through all the generations till today. I feel as if I had been there myself, and seen the Holy One who came to save the souls of those that do daily beat and ill-use us."

"Tell me," said the ass's colt, "for I am young! What were They like, the Mother and her Babe?"

The steer said: "She wore a white wimple, with a crown on it, and a blue robe with the Magnificat broidered about its border. And He had a golden orb in His right hand, and a light round His head; and as soon as He was born He spoke to her."

"What did he say?" asked the colt.

"He said, 'Hail Mary, the Lord is with thee!' And at that the father of my fathers and the father of your fathers bent their knees, and began worshipping Him. And ever since then, once a year, our hearts are opened, so that we know how to worship Him and do Him meet service. But not in this world shall we learn to serve Him daily, as men do; and not for many worlds to serve him continually, as the angels do."

"When men have become as angels," said the colt, "perhaps we shall be in the place of men. How good it will be, then, to serve Him daily!"

"Good indeed!" replied the steer. "Kneel down; we are near the hour of the blissful Birth."

Said the colt: "Was there no trouble at that Birth?"

"I do not know," answered the steer; "but the meek Mother did not cry, nor the Babe, when It was born, wail."

Presently, while the beasts bent worshipping there, a shuddering cry came from the straw; again and again it was repeated, and the beasts knew and recognized the great central note of nature since the Fall, the cry of a mother in her pains. By and by was added to it the cry of a human when it first draws breath. Feeble and weak, Molly stretched out her arms, and caught and laid the naked life in her breast.

The steer and the ass's colt looked on with mild and reverent fear. "The Holy Child and His Mother," said they, "have sent us these to watch and guard for a remembrance of Them."

They heard the mother moan, "Bring water, and a priest, lest my child die in sin, and be not baptized into Christ!" And as midnight grew near, they heard her say again, "It dies, it dies! Oh, for a priest, and a drop of water!"

Then for the love of Christ, on this night of His birth, the steer and the ass's colt rose up to do Him service. They went out softly by the door that lay ajar, and stole down side by side to the church that shone lighted below the hill.

All the way, over their heads, shone the Northern Lights with flicker and throb: and they knew that there, out of gold harp-strings like corn, angels were reaping melodies to God. When they got to the church it was the time of the midnight Mass. Looking in through a window they saw the Crib, and all the congregation kneeling before it. Our Lady had on a white wimple, with a gold crown on it, and a blue robe; and the Holy Child held an orb, and wore a halo round His head.

Then the two beasts beat softly upon the door with their forefeet; and the steer lowed, and the ass brayed for the priest to come out and carry Christ to the child's soul.

One of the servers came out to drive them away: but they bore all his strokes patiently, and stayed there waiting for the priest to come forth. "Let us wait quietly!" said the steer at last. "When the Mass is over he will come."

So silently they watched, and heard the Sanctus sung, and bowed themselves at sacring-bell; till presently the congregation came out, and last of all the priest.

The priest was in a hurry to get back to his bed and be warm;

and lo, and behold, down knelt the ass right in the way before his feet! Whichever way he turned, there the steer and the ass hemmed him in.

Soon the priest began thinking, what marvel was this? Had the two beasts that worshipped at Christ's cradle been sent by God, in reward to him for his services, to bear him home? "Non dignus sum!" said he, crossing himself; and therewith he sat himself on the back of the beast, and rode.

Ass and steer walked on together; but when they came to the dividing of the ways that led to the priest's house, and to the farm, by no means could the priest get himself brought nearer where he would be. There in the cross-roads the colt danced him round like a wind-worshipping weather-cock.

At length, so stirred was he with resentment at the brute so ill-fulfilling the heavenly dictates of its mission, that lifting up his staff he struck the colt roundly three times, bidding it go on in the name of the Blessed Trinity.

And thereat his eyes were opened, and he saw One leading the ass in the way up to the farm. And she had on a blue robe, and a white wimple with a crown over it, and a Child on her arm bearing an orb; and light rayed round them.

Then the priest was so stricken with fear, that he tried with all his courage to fall off the colt, but could not; and presently at the crest of the hill they turned in by the farmyard gate. Then the ass stood still, and the priest found his feet trembling on firm ground.

Over the heavens shot the Northern Lights, wherein were the angels making melodies to God; but within the stable was more light than came from them. Looking in, he saw that the ass and the steer had entered, and were bowed forward upon their knees; and between them was she of the blue robe and wimple and crown, bearing a Babe.

The priest fell face forward to the earth; and when he lifted himself there was no light within the stable save that which came from the Northern Lights: and he entering saw a young mother lying asleep, with a new-born babe in her arms.

But around and over her poor clothing lay the white wimple, and the blue robe broidered with the words of the Magnificat: the same which he had seen worn by Her who went before, leading the ass, and bearing the Blessed Child.

The
Old Lady's
Story

by
E. LYNN LINTON
(1822–1890)

The 1850s were a particularly fruitful period for Christmas stories in Britain, as Dickens' success prompted others to try to make good on the public's growing appetite for the sensational. Dickens himself put together a special collection annually for the Christmas edition of his Household Words, *drawing on his friends and fellow-writers for their contributions. He had a particular admiration for the abilities as a writer of E. Lynn Linton (then known as Eliza Lynn), and "The Old Lady's Story" is an especially fine example of the macabre, so loved by the mid-Victorians. I am also particularly pleased to include this story here as, so far as I can see, it has not been reprinted since its original inclusion in Dickens' Christmas number of 1853.*

From
Another Round of Stories by the Christmas Fire,
being the extra Christmas number of
Household Words *(1853),*
conducted by Charles Dickens.

I have never told you my secret, my dear nieces. However, this Christmas, which may well be the last to an old woman, I will give the whole story; for though it is a strange story, and a sad one, it is true; and what sin there was in it I trust I may have expiated by my tears and my repentance. Perhaps the last expiation of all is this painful confession.

We were very young at the time, Lucy and I, and the neighbours said we were pretty. So we were, I believe, though entirely different; for Lucy was quiet, and fair, and I was full of life and spirits; wild beyond any power of control, and reckless. I was the elder by two years; but more fit to be in leading-strings myself than to guide or govern my sister. But she was so good, so quiet, and so wise, that she needed no one's guidance; for if advice was to be given, it was she who gave it, not I; and I never knew her judgment or perception fail. She was the darling of the house. My mother had died soon after Lucy was born. A picture in the dining-room of her, in spite of all the difference of dress, was exactly like Lucy; and, as Lucy was now seventeen and my mother had been only eighteen when it was taken, there was no discrepancy of years.

One Allhallow's eve a party of us—all young girls, not one of us twenty years of age—were trying our fortunes round the drawing-room fire; throwing nuts into the brightest blaze, to hear if mythic He's loved any of us, and in what proportion; or pouring hot lead into water, to find cradles and rings, or purses and coffins; or breaking the whites of eggs into tumblers half full of water, and then drawing up the white into pictures of the future—the prettiest experiment of all. I remember Lucy could only make a recumbent figure of hers, like a marble monument in miniature; and I, a maze of masks and skulls and things that looked like dancing apes or imps, and vapoury lines that did not require much imagination to fashion into ghosts or spirits; for they were clearly human in the outline, but thin and vapoury. And we all laughed a great deal, and teazed one another, and were as full of fun and mischief, and innocence and thoughtlessness, as a nest of young birds.

There was a certain room at the other end of our rambling old manor-house, which was said to be haunted, and which my father had therefore discontinued as a dwelling-room, so that we children might not be frightened by foolish servants; and he had made it into a lumber-place—a kind of ground-floor granary—where no one had any business. Well, it was proposed that one of us should go into this room alone, lock the door, stand before a glass, pare and eat an apple very deliberately, looking fixedly in the glass all the time; and then, if the mind never once wandered, the future husband would be clearly shown in the glass. As I was always the foolhardy girl of every party, and was, moreover, very desirous of seeing that apocryphal individual, my future husband (whose non-appearance I used to wonder at and bewail in secret), I was glad enough to make the trial, notwithstanding the entreaties of some of the more timid. Lucy, above all, clung to me, and besought me earnestly not to go—at last, almost with tears. But my pride of courage, and my curiosity, and a certain nameless feeling of attraction, were too strong for me. I laughed Lucy and her abettors into silence; uttered half a dozen bravados; and, taking up a bed-room candle, passed through the long silent passages, to the cold, dark, deserted room—my heart beating with excitement, my foolish head dizzy with hope and faith. The church-clock chimed a quarter past twelve as I opened the door.

It was an awful night. The windows shook, as if every instant they would burst in with some strong man's hand on the bars, and his shoulder against the frames; and the trees howled and shrieked, as if each branch were sentient and in pain. The ivy beat against the window, sometimes with fury, and sometimes with the leaves slowly scraping against the glass, and drawing out long shrill sounds, like spirits crying to each other. In the room itself it was worse. Rats had made it their refuge for many years, and they rushed behind the wainscot and down inside the walls, bringing with them showers of lime and dust, which rattled like chains, or sounded like men's feet hurrying to and fro; and every now and then a cry broke through the room, one could not tell from where or from what, but a cry, distinct and human; heavy blows seemed to be struck on the floor, which cracked like parting ice beneath my feet, and loud knockings shook the walls. Yet in this tumult, I was not afraid. I reasoned on each new sound very calmly—and said, "Those are rats," or "those are leaves," and "birds in the chimney," or "owls in the ivy," as each new howl or scream struck my ear. And I was not in the least frightened or disturbed; it all seemed natural and familiar. I placed the candle on a table in the midst of the room, where an old broken mirror stood; and, looking steadily into the glass (having first wiped off the dust), I began to eat Eve's forbidden fruit, wishing intently, as I had been bidden, for the apparition of my future husband.

In about ten minutes I heard a dull, vague, unearthly sound; felt, not heard. It was as if countless wings rushed by, and small low voices whispering too; as if a crowd, a multitude of life was about me; as if shadowy faces crushed up against me, and eyes and hands, and sneering lips, all mocked me. I was suffocated. The air was so heavy—so filled with life, that I could not breathe. I was pressed on from all sides, and could not turn nor move without parting thickening vapours. I heard my own name—I can swear to that to-day! I heard it repeated through the room; and then bursts of laughter followed, and the wings rustled and fluttered, and the whispering voices mocked and chattered, and the heavy air, so filled with life, hung heavier and thicker, and the Things pressed up to me closer, and checked the breath on my lips with the clammy breath from theirs.

I was not alarmed. I was not excited; but I was fascinated and spell-bound; yet with every sense seeming to possess ten times its natural power. I still went on looking in the glass—still earnestly desiring an apparition—when suddenly I saw a man's face peering over my shoulder in the glass. Girls, I could draw that face to this hour! The low forehead, with the short curling hair, black as jet, growing down in a sharp point; the dark eyes, beneath thick eyebrows, burning with a peculiar light; the nose and the dilating nostrils; the thin lips, curled into a smile—I see them all plainly before me now. And—O, the smile that it was!—the mockery and sneer, the derision, the sarcasm, the contempt, the victory that were in it!—even then it struck into me a sense of submission. The eyes looked full into mine: those eyes and mine fastened on each other; and, as I ended my task, the church clock chimed the half-hour; and, suddenly released, as if from a spell, I turned round, expecting to see a living man standing beside me. But I met only the chill air coming in from the loose window, and the solitude of the dark night. The Life had gone; the wings had rushed away; the voices had died out, and I was alone; with the rats behind the wainscot, the owls hooting in the ivy, and the wind howling through the trees.

Convinced that either some trick had been played me, or that some one was concealed in the room, I searched every corner of it. I lifted lids of boxes filled with the dust of ages and with rotting paper lying like bleaching skin. I took down the chimney-board, and soot and ashes flew up in clouds. I opened dim old closets, where all manner of foul insects had made their homes, and where daylight had not entered for generations: but I found nothing. Satisfied that nothing human was in the room, and that no one could have been there to-night—nor for many months, if not years—and still nerved to a state of desperate courage, I went back to the drawing-room. But, as I left that room I felt that something flowed out with me; and, all through the long passages, I retained the sensation that this something was behind me. My steps were heavy; the consciousness of pursuit having paralysed, not quickened me; for I knew that when I left that haunted room I had not left it alone. As I opened the drawing-room door—the blazing fire and the strong lamp-light bursting out upon me with a peculiar expression of cheerfulness and welcome—I heard a laugh close at my elbow, and felt a hot blast across my neck. I started back, but the laugh died away, and all I saw were two points of light, fiery and flaming, that somehow fashioned themselves into eyes beneath their heavy brows, and looked at me meaningly through the darkness.

They all wanted to know what I had seen; but I refused to say a word; not liking to tell a falsehood then, and not liking to expose myself to ridicule. For I felt that what I had seen was true, and that no sophistry and no argument, no reasoning and no ridicule, could shake my belief in it. My sweet Lucy came up to me—seeing me look so pale and wild—threw her arms round my neck, and leaned forward to kiss me. As she bent her head, I felt the same warm blast rush over my lips, and my sister cried, "Why, Lizzie, your lips burn like fire!"

And so they did, and for long after. The Presence was with me still, never leaving me day nor night: by my pillow, its whispering voice often waking me from wild dreams; by my side, in the broad sunlight; by my side, in the still moonlight; never absent, busy at my brain, busy at my heart—a form ever banded to me. It flitted like a cold cloud between my sweet sister's eyes and mine, and dimmed them so that I could scarcely see their beauty. It drowned my father's voice; and his words fell confused and indistinct.

Not long after, a stranger came into our neighbourhood. He bought Green Howe, a deserted old property by the river-side, where no one had lived for many many years; not since the young bride, Mrs. Braithwaite, had been found in the river one morning, entangled among the dank weeds and dripping alders, strangled and drowned, and her husband dead—none knew how—lying by the chapel door. The place had had a bad name ever since, and no one would live there. However, it was said that a stranger, who had been long in the East, a Mr. Felix, had now bought it, and that he was coming to reside there. And, true enough, one day the whole of our little town of Thornhill was in a state of excitement; for a travelling-carriage and four, followed by another full of servants—Hindoos, or Lascars, or Negroes; dark-coloured, strange-looking people—passed through, and Mr. Felix took possession of Green Howe.

My father called on him after a time; and I, as the mistress of the house, went with him. Green Howe had been changed, as if by magic, and we both said so together, as we entered the iron

gates that led up the broad walk. The ruined garden was one
mass of plants, fresh and green, many of them quite new to me;
and the shrubbery, which had been a wilderness, was restored
to order. The house looked larger than before, now that it was
so beautifully decorated; and the broken trellis-work, which
used to hang dangling among the ivy, was matted with creeping
roses, and jasmine, which left on me the impression of having
been in flower, which was impossible. It was a fairy palace; and
we could scarcely believe that this was the deserted, ill-omened
Green Howe. The foreign servants, too, in Eastern dresses, covered with rings, and necklaces, and earrings; the foreign smells
of sandal-wood, and camphor, and musk; the curtains that hung
everywhere in place of doors, some of velvet, and some of cloth
of gold; the air of luxury, such as I, a simple country girl, had
never seen before, made such a powerful impression on me, that
I felt as if carried away to some unknown region. As we entered,
Mr. Felix came to meet us; and, drawing aside a heavy curtain
that seemed all of gold and fire—for the flame-coloured flowers
danced and quivered on the gold—he led us into an inner
room, where the darkened light; the atmosphere heavy with
perfumes; the statues; the birds like living jewels; the magnifi-
cence of stuffs, and the luxuriousness of arrangement, overpowered me. I felt as if I had sunk into a lethargy, in which I heard
only the rich voice, and saw only the fine form of our stranger
host.

He was certainly very handsome; tall, dark, yet pale as marble: his very lips were pale; with eyes that were extremely
bright; but which had an expression behind them that subdued
me. His manners were graceful. He was very cordial to us, and
made us stay a long time; taking us through his grounds to see
his improvements, and pointing out here and there further alter-
ations to be made; all with such a disregard for local difficulties,
and for cost, that, had he been one of the princes of the genii he
could not have talked more royally. He was more than merely
attentive to me; speaking to me often and in a lower voice,
bending down near to me, and looking at me with eyes that
thrilled through every nerve and fibre. I saw that my father was
uneasy; and, when we left, I asked him how he liked our new
neighbour. He said, "Not much, Lizzie," with a grave and almost

displeased look, as if he had probed the weakness I was scarcely conscious of myself. I thought at the time that he was harsh.

However, as there was nothing positively to object to in Mr. Felix, my father's impulse of distrust could not well be indulged without rudeness; and my dear father was too thoroughly a gentleman ever to be rude even to his enemy. We therefore saw a great deal of the stranger; who established himself in our house on the most familiar footing, and forced on my father and Lucy an intimacy they both disliked but could not avoid. For it was forced with such consummate skill and tact, that there was nothing which the most rigid could object to.

I gradually became an altered being under his influence. In one thing only a happier—in the loss of the Voice and the Form which had haunted me. Since I had known Felix this terror had gone. The reality had absorbed the shadow. But in nothing else was this strange man's influence over me beneficial. I remember that I used to hate myself for my excessive irritability of temper when I was away from him. Everything at home displeased me. Everything seemed so small and mean and old and poor after the lordly glory of that house; and the very caresses of my family and olden school-day friends were irksome and hateful to me. All except my Lucy lost its charm; and to her I was faithful as ever; to her I never changed. But her influence seemed to war with his, wonderfully. When with him I felt borne away in a torrent. His words fell upon me mysterious and thrilling, and he gave me fleeting glimpses into worlds which had never opened themselves to me before; glimpses seen and gone like the Arabian gardens.

When I came back to my sweet sister, her pure eyes and the holy light that lay in them, her gentle voice speaking of the sacred things of heaven and the earnest things of life, seemed to me like a former existence: a state I had lived in years ago. But this divided influence nearly killed me; it seemed to part my very soul and wrench my being in twain; and this, more than all the rest, made me sad beyond anything people believed possible in one so gay and reckless as I had been.

My father's dislike to Felix increased daily; and Lucy, who had never been known to use a harsh word in her life, from the first refused to believe a thought of good in him, or to allow him one single claim to praise. She used to cling to me in a wild, beseeching way, and entreat me with prayers, such as a mother might have poured out before an erring child, to stop in time, and to return to those who loved me. "For your soul is lost from among us, Lizzie," she used to say; "and nothing but a frame remains of the full life of love you once gave us!" But one word, one look, from Felix was enough to make me forget every ear and every prayer of her who, until now, had been my idol and my law.

At last my dear father commanded me not to see Felix again. I felt as if I should have died. In vain I wept and prayed. In vain I gave full license to my thoughts, and suffered words to pour from my lips which ought never to have crept into my heart. In vain; my father was inexorable.

I was in the drawing-room. Suddenly, noiselessly, Felix was beside me. He had not entered by the door which was directly in front of me; and the window was closed. I never could understand this sudden appearance; for I am certain that he had not been concealed.

"Your father has spoken of me, Lizzie?" he said with a singular smile. I was silent.

"And has forbidden you to see me again?" he continued.

"Yes," I answered, impelled to speak by something stronger than my will.

"And you intend to obey him?"

"No," I said again, in the same manner, as if I had been talking in a dream.

He smiled again. Who was he so like when he smiled? I could not remember, and yet I knew that he was like some one I had seen—a face that hovered outside my memory, on the horizon, and never floated near enough to be distinctly realised.

"You are right, Lizzie," he then said; "there are ties which are stronger than a father's commands—ties which no man has the right, and no man has the power to break. Meet me to-morrow at noon in the Low Lane; we will speak further."

He did not say this in any supplicating, nor in any loving manner: it was simply a command, unaccompanied by one tender word or look. He had never said he loved me—never; it seemed to be too well understood between us to need assurances.

I answered, "Yes," burying my face in my hands, in shame at this my first act of disobedience to my father; and, when I raised my head, he was gone. Gone as he had entered, without a foot-fall sounding ever so lightly.

I met him the next day; and it was not the only time that I did so. Day after day I stole at his command from the house, to walk with him in the Low Lane—the lane which the country people said was haunted, and which was consequently always deserted. And there we used to walk or sit under the blighted elm tree for hours;—he talking, but I not understanding all he said: for there was a tone of grandeur and of mystery in his words that overpowered without enlightening me, and that left my spirit dazzled rather than convinced. I had to give reasons at home for my long absences, and he bade me say that I had been with old Dame Todd, the blind widow of Thornhill Rise, and that I had been reading the Bible to her. And I obeyed; although, while I said it, I felt Lucy's eyes fixed plaintively on mine, and heard her murmur a prayer that I might be forgiven.

Lucy grew ill. As the flowers and the summer sun came on, her spirit faded more rapidly away. I have known since, that it was grief more than malady which was killing her. The look of nameless suffering, which used to be in her face, has haunted me through life with undying sorrow. It was suffering that I, who ought to have rather died for her, had caused. But not even her illness stayed me. In the intervals I nursed her tenderly and lovingly as before; but for hours and hours I left her—all through the long days of summer—to walk in the Low Lane, and to sit in my world of poetry and fire. When I came back my sister was often weeping, and I knew that it was for me—I, who once would have given my life to save her from one hour of sor-row. Then I would fling myself on my knees beside her, in an agony of shame and repentance, and promise better things of the morrow, and vow strong efforts against the power and the spell that were on me. But the morrow subjected me to the same unhallowed fascination, the same faithlessness.

At last Felix told me that I must come with him; that I must leave my home, and take part in his life; that I belonged to him and to him only, and that I could not break the tablet of a fate ordained; that I was his destiny, and he mine, and that I must fulfil the law which the stars had written in the sky. I fought against this. I spoke of my father's anger, and of my sister's illness. I prayed to him for pity, not to force this on me, and knelt in the shadows of the autumn sunset to ask from him forbearance.

I did not yield this day, nor the next, nor for many days. At last he conquered. When I said "Yes" he kissed the scarf I wore round my neck. Until then he had never touched even my hand with his lips. I consented to leave my sister, who I well knew was dying; I consented to leave my father, whose whole life had been one act of love and care for his children; and to bring a stain on our name, unstained until then. I consented to leave those who loved me—all I loved—for a stranger.

All was prepared; the hurrying clouds, lead-coloured, and the howling wind, the fit companions in nature with the evil and the despair of my soul. Lucy was worse to-day; but though I felt going to my death, in leaving her, I could not resist. Had his voice called me to the scaffold, I must have gone. It was the last day of October, and at midnight when I was to leave the house. I had kissed my sleeping sister, who was dreaming in her sleep, and cried, and grasped my hand, and called aloud, "Lizzie, Lizzie! Come back!" But the spell was on me, and I left her; and still her dreaming voice called out, choking with sobs, "Not there! not there, Lizzie! Come back to me!"

I was to leave the house by the large, old, haunted room that I have spoken of before; Felix waiting for me outside. And, a little after twelve o'clock, I opened the door to pass through. This time the chill, and the damp, and the darkness unnerved me. The broken mirror was in the middle of the room, as before, and, in passing it, I mechanically raised my eyes. Then I remembered that it was Allhallow's eve, the anniversary of the apparition of last year. As I looked, the room, which had been so deadly still, became filled with the sound I had heard before. The rushing of large wings, and the crowd of whispering voices flowed like a river round me; and again, glaring into my eyes, was the same face in the glass that I had seen before, the sneering smile even more triumphant, the blighting stare of the fiery eyes, the low brow and the coal-black hair, and the look of mockery. All were there; and all I had seen before and since; for it was Felix who was gazing at me from the glass. When I turned to speak to him, the room was empty. Not a living creature was there; only a low laugh, and the far-off voices whispering, and the wings. And then a hand tapped on the window, and the voice of Felix cried from outside, "Come, Lizzie, come!"

I staggered, rather than walked, to the window; and, as I was close to it—my hand raised to open it—there stood between me and it a pale figure clothed in white; her face more pale than the linen round it. Her hair hung down on her breast, and her blue eyes looked earnestly and mournfully into mine. She was silent, and yet it seemed as if a volume of love and of entreaty flowed from her lips; as if I heard words of deathless affection. It was Lucy; standing there in this bitter midnight cold—giving her life to save me. Felix called to me again, impatiently; and, as he called, the figure turned, and beckoned me; beckoning me gently, lovingly, beseechingly; and then slowly faded away. The chime of the half-hour sounded; and, I fled from the room to my sister. I found her lying dead on the floor; her hair hanging over her breast, and one hand stretched out as if in supplication.

The next day Felix disappeared; he and his whole retinue; and Green Howe fell into ruins again. No one knew where he went, as no one knew from whence he came. And to this day I sometimes doubt whether or not he was a clever adventurer, who had heard of my father's wealth: and who, seeing my weak and imaginative character, had acted on it for his own purposes. All that I do know is that my sister's spirit saved me from ruin; and that she died to save me. She had seen and known all, and gave herself for my salvation down to the last and supreme effort she made to rescue me. She died at that hour of half-past twelve; and at half-past twelve, as I live before you all, she appeared to me and recalled me.

And this is the reason why I never married, and why I pass Allhallow's eve in prayer by my sister's grave. I have told you to-night this story of mine, because I feel that I shall not live over another last night of October, but that before the next white Christmas roses come out like winter stars on the earth I shall be at peace in the grave. Not in the grave; let me rather hope with my blessed sister in Heaven!

The
True Meaning
of **Crumbfest**

by
DAVID WEALE
(1942–   )

This story comes from a lovely little book called An Island Christmas Reader, *a collection of stories about Christmas on Prince Edward Island. "The True Meaning of Crumbfest" is the story of Eckhart the mouse, and of his strange unravelling of the wonders of Crumbfest—a season of great micely celebration when crumbs (not just bread or biscuit, but cake, cookies and pie-crust!) are mysteriously plentiful, and when the world "between the walls" seems suddenly a cheerier place.*

his is the story of young Eckhart, a mouse. He had quick tiny feet, shiny black eyes and an extra-long tail. Eckhart lived with his family in a place called Rose Valley, Prince Edward Island.

It is also the story of a very great mystery; a mystery which all the mice in Rose Valley talked about, but which was never solved until the day Eckhart set off on his great adventure. It was the day he went boldly where no mouse had gone before, and discovered the true meaning of Crumbfest.

For Eckhart and the other mice, every year was divided into two parts: the Outside part, and the Inside part. During the long warm days they lived in a snug burrow beneath a spruce tree in the corner of a field, next to the woods. But when the days became shorter, and the great snows came, they left Outside and moved Inside, between the walls of the big white farmhouse where the people lived. The mice, of course, didn't refer to them as people. They called them "the straight ones," because of the way they walked.

Eckhart didn't like going Inside. None of the mice did. The narrow space between the walls, where they spent the winter, was a cold, dismal place. There was no grass there, or trees, or flowers; and no sunshine.

The Inside was also a hungry place. There was plenty of food in the house, but at night, the only time it was safe to go searching, it was almost always shut up in the little pantry off the kitchen—in jars, or in tins with tight covers. The only spot the mice could find food was on the kitchen floor, underneath the big wooden table where the people ate. There would usually be a few crumbs there, tiny bits of bread or biscuit which had tumbled down from above.

But there was one time of the year when all that changed.

Every year, in late December, just a few weeks after the mice had moved Inside, a most astonishing thing happened. Suddenly! as if by magic, there were crumbs everywhere. For several days the mice feasted, not just on bread or biscuit, but on cake, and cookies, and pie-crust.

The mice had a name for this time of abundance. They called it Crumbfest, and over the years it became the most important celebration in mouse society. "Merry Crumbfest," they would call out to one another as they scurried in and out of their hole in the wall, bringing back load after load of tasty morsels.

The young mice, like Eckhart, who had been born Outside during the summer, had only heard stories about Crumbfest, and so they looked forward to it with almost unbearable excitement. "Is it really as crumby as they say?" Eckhart asked his mother. "Oh yes, dear," she would answer, "it is the crumbiest time of the whole year."

Eckhart's grandfather, a skinny bent old mouse named Tomis, had lived longer than any of the other mice. He had celebrated three Crumbfests, and Eckhart asked him once why it happened every year. Old Tomis said he didn't know. He said it was a mystery. When Eckhart asked him a second time he twitched his tail in annoyance. "Don't ask so many questions," he said crossly. "Crumbfest happens, and that's all there is to it! Just be thankful, and don't waste your time trying to know things that mice can never know.

"I'm warning you, Master Eckhart," he added in a serious voice, "if you ask too many questions you may just ruin it for yourself and everyone else."

Eckhart felt puzzled and hurt. He didn't like to upset his grandfather, but he just wasn't satisfied with the old mouse's answer. Eckhart, you see, was a most curious creature. Indeed, his mother had told him once that his curiosity was just as long as his tail, and that one day it would get him into trouble.

The truth is, Eckhart had some doubts about Crumbfest. He thought maybe it was just a story the old mice had made up to help pass the time during the long, dark, Inside days. He once told his little sister, Mavis, that there was no such thing as Crumbfest, and she burst into tears. "Eckhart," she sobbed, "you are a hateful, horrid brother."

But then, one day, just when Eckhart was beginning to feel certain that he was right, the crumbs appeared.

It was amazing! Absolutely amazing!

The word spread quickly between the walls. "They've arrived! They've arrived!" everyone was saying. "The crumbs are here!"

Eckhart had never seen such excitement. Everyone was happy. Even Tomis, who hardly ever smiled, seemed to be in a good mood. And no one was more joyous than Eckhart. His dark little eyes were shining with delight as mouse after mouse came scampering back through the hole in the wall, cheeks bulging with delicious holiday goodies.

But all of that just made Eckhart even more curious. On the second day of Crumbfest, as he sat chewing on a big sticky raisin, he started thinking again about the reason for this most mysterious event. Right there and then he decided he must solve the riddle. He made up his mind to go exploring.

When he told some of the other mice about his intentions they looked at him in astonishment, and his friend Martin told him he was crazy. Everyone said it was just too dangerous.

When grandfather Tomis learned of Eckhart's plan he shook his head and said scoldingly, "You stubborn little scallywag, how long is it going to take you to learn your place in this world? I've told you over and over that mice are creatures of the Outside, and that we are not meant to know the secrets of the Inside. Besides, there's too much danger in it. It's too risky—far too risky!"

Old Tomis dropped his head and continued muttering in his whiskers. It seemed he had forgotten all about Eckhart, and was talking to himself. Without saying a word, Eckhart left the old mouse. He scurried to the hole in the wall and out into the kitchen.

It was the middle of the night and the room was quite dark. But there was a moon Outside, and it shone through the windows, giving Eckhart just enough light to see where he was going.

It was also very quiet. Not a creature was stirring—except Eckhart.

He passed beneath the great wooden table. This was familiar territory, and he paused for a moment to decide where he would go from there. He looked across the room and saw a door leading into a hallway. Beyond that was the unknown, and, perhaps, the secret of Crumbfest. He knew that was where he must go.

As he passed through the doorway he could feel his heart pounding. He moved slowly at first, but then scampered across a mat and came to another door. He stopped and peered inside, twitching his nose, for he had become aware of a familiar scent in the air. In front of him was a wide room, with a shiny floor. There was a very large object near the door; something he had never seen before. He scampered underneath and poked his head out the other side.

And that's when he saw it!

Eckhart could scarcely believe his eyes. He looked again, but sure enough, it was still there.

It was a tree. A fir tree. A beautiful tree from the Outside was right there in front of him—on the Inside.

Eckhart ran over quickly and looked up into the branches.

There, on the tree, were other things from the Outside. There was a long string of red berries—the kind that grow on the rose bushes along the fence—and some birds. They didn't look exactly like the birds he had seen Outside, but they were definitely birds, sitting very still in the branches.

It was all very surprising, and strange, and something told Eckhart that it must have something to do with Crumbfest, though he wasn't sure what.

There was a small table beside the tree and Eckhart ran quickly up one of the legs to get a better view. When he came up over the top there was another great surprise waiting for him. There, gathered together in a circle, were tiny animals from the Outside.

There were two cows, a horse with long ears and several sheep. There were also some tiny people there, and right in the middle a little box, with a baby sleeping in some straw. Eckhart walked over slowly and stood beside one of the sheep, which was just exactly the same size as he was. He remained there quietly for a few moments, standing just as still as the other animals.

And that's when it happened!

Eckhart felt something he had never felt before. It started somewhere inside of him, and spread out right to the very tips of all his whiskers, and to the end of his extra-long tail.

It wasn't exactly astonishment, and it wasn't exactly joy. It was wonder—that's what it was. Eckhart felt wonder-full.

It only lasted a short time, but Eckhart knew in that moment that he had discovered the meaning of Crumbfest. It came to him in a flash, and he knew his journey was over. It was now time to go back to the other mice and tell them his story.

He scampered down to the floor, and, with one last look at the tree, ran quickly—

> across the shiny floor,
> under the large object,
> out through the door,
> across the mat,
> through the other door,
> under the great table where the crumbs were,
> and into the hole in the corner.

When he arrived back between the walls the other mice could tell immediately that something sensational had happened. Eckhart had been away a half an hour—which is quite a long time for a mouse—and he looked different. Soon they were all gathered around him.

"Where have you been?" they asked. "What have you seen?" Even grandfather Tomis, looking especially interested, came close enough to hear.

Eckhart told them the story of his journey. He told them about the big room, the tree, the berries and the birds. And when he got to the part about the animals he lowered his head, straightened his tail, and said softly, "The mystery of Crumbfest is the mystery of the Outside and the Inside. When the Outside comes Inside it is a special time, for when the Outside and the Inside are together, Crumbfest happens."

For a moment no one spoke.

Most of the mice looked puzzled. And Tomis scowled. But there were a few whose eyes opened very wide, as though they had just heard a secret which they already knew.

In the years that followed, the story of Eckhart's adventure was passed down from generation to generation. The telling and retelling of the tale became an important part of the Crumbfest celebrations. Most of the mice still didn't go farther than the crumbs beneath the table, but there were a few who followed Eckhart's trail through the doorway. Like Eckhart they experienced for themselves the mystery of Crumbfest, and the wonder of a place where the Inside and the Outside are together.

Karl's
Christmas Cake

This recipe was given to me by Nancy and David O'Connor, who taught school in Lahr, West Germany after the war. It is excellent, and an annual Christmas favourite in our home. Drink it or cook it, as you prefer—but save a few bits for Eckhart!

Karl's Christmas Cake

3—12 oz. pkg. of raisins
3—12 oz. pkg. of mixed fruit and peel
2—8 oz. pkg. of glazed cherries (red and green)
1—1 lb. can of mixed nuts (no peanuts)
1—8 oz. pkg. of glazed pineapple
1—each lemon and orange finely chopped

Soak for 2 days in:

1 cup honey	1 cup dark rum
2 cups sherry	1 cup strong coffee
1 cup brandy	1/2 cup Grand Marnier

Serve on ice cream, and forget
the baking,

OR

Cream 1 lb. butter and 1 cup sugar.
Mix in 12 eggs well beaten.
Sift 3 1/2 cups flour, 2 tsp. cinnamon, and 1/2 tsp. each of
baking soda, allspice, ginger and cloves.
Add half to fruit mixture and stir, and other half to egg and
butter.
Then mix all together.

Bake for four hours at 250°-275°F in
pans lined with greased brown paper
(use shortening). Test to see if baked
(baking time may be shorter,
depending on your oven). Makes
twenty pounds.

The **Happy Prince**

by
OSCAR WILDE
(1854–1900)

"The Happy Prince" is one of Wilde's perfect little parables—well-suited to a Christmas theme. A simple story of generosity in the face of personal suffering.

igh above the city, on a tall column, stood the statue of the Happy Prince. He was gilded all over with thin leaves of fine gold, for eyes he had two bright sapphires, and a large red ruby glowed on his sword-hilt.

He was very much admired indeed. "He is as beautiful as a weathercock," remarked one of the Town Councillors who wished to gain a reputation for having artistic tastes; "only not quite so useful," he added, fearing lest people should think him unpractical, which he really was not.

"Why can't you be like the Happy Prince?" asked a sensible mother of her little boy who was crying for the moon. "The Happy Prince never dreams of crying for anything."

"I am glad there is some one in the world who is quite happy," muttered a disappointed man as he gazed at the wonderful statue.

"He looks just like an angel," said the Charity Children as they came out of the cathedral in their bright scarlet cloaks and their clean white pinafores.

"How do you know?" said the Mathematical Master, "you have never seen one."

"Ah! but we have, in our dreams," answered the children; and the Mathematical Master frowned and looked very severe, for he did not approve of children dreaming.

One night there flew over the city a little Swallow. His friends had gone away to Egypt six weeks before, but he had stayed behind, for he was in love with the most beautiful Reed. He had met her early in the spring as he was flying down the river after a big yellow moth, and had been so attracted by her slender waist that he had stopped to talk to her.

"Shall I love you?" said the Swallow, who liked to come to the point at once, and the Reed made him a low bow. So he flew round and round her, touching the water with his wings, and making silver ripples. This was his courtship, and it lasted all through the summer.

"It is a ridiculous attachment," twittered the other Swallows; "she has no money, and far too many relations;" and indeed the river was quite full of Reeds. Then, when the autumn came they all flew away.

After they had gone he felt lonely, and began to tire of his lady-love. "She has no conversation," he said, "and I am afraid that she is a coquette, for she is always flirting with the wind." And certainly, whenever the wind blew, the Reed made the most graceful curtseys. "I admit that she is domestic," he continued, "but I love travelling, and my wife, consequently, should love travelling also."

"Will you come away with me?" he said finally to her, but the Reed shook her head, she was so attached to her home.

"You have been trifling with me," he cried. "I am off to the Pyramids. Good-bye!" and he flew away.

All day long he flew, and at night-time he arrived at the city. "Where shall I put up?" he said; "I hope the town has made preparations."

Then he saw the statue on the tall column.

"I will put up there," he cried; "it is a fine position, with plenty of fresh air." So he alighted just between the feet of the Happy Prince.

"I have a golden bedroom," he said softly to himself as he looked round, and he prepared to go to sleep; but just as he was putting his head under his wing a large drop of water fell on him. "What a curious thing!" he cried; "there is not a single cloud in the sky, the stars are quite clear and bright, and yet it is raining. The climate in the north of Europe is really dreadful. The Reed used to like the rain, but that was merely her selfishness."

Then another drop fell.

"What is the use of a statue if it cannot keep the rain off?" he said; "I must look for a good chimney-pot," and he determined to fly away.

But before he had opened his wings, a third drop fell, and he looked up, and saw—Ah! what did he see?

The eyes of the Happy Prince were filled with tears, and tears were running down his golden cheeks. His face was so beautiful in the moonlight that the little Swallow was filled with pity.

"Who are you?" he said.

"I am the Happy Prince."

"Why are you weeping then?" asked the Swallow; "you have quite drenched me."

"When I was alive and had a human heart," answered the statue, "I did not know what tears were, for I lived in the Palace of Sans-Souci, where sorrow is not allowed to enter. In the day-time I played with my companions in the garden, and in the evening I led the dance in the Great Hall. Round the garden ran a very lofty wall, but I never cared to ask what lay beyond it, everything about me was so beautiful. My courtiers called me the Happy Prince, and happy indeed I was, if pleasure be happiness. So I lived, and so I died. And now that I am dead they have set me up here so high that I can see all the ugliness and all the misery of my city, and though my heart is made of lead yet I cannot choose but weep."

"What! is he not solid gold?" said the Swallow to himself. He was too polite to make any personal remarks out loud.

"Far away," continued the statue in a low musical voice, "far away in a little street there is a poor house. One of the windows is open, and through it I can see a woman seated at a table. Her face is thin and worn, and she has coarse, red hands, all pricked by the needle, for she is a seamstress. She is embroidering passion-flowers on a satin gown for the loveliest of the Queen's maids-of-honour to wear at the next Court-ball. In a bed in the corner of the room her little boy is lying ill. He has a fever, and is asking for oranges. His mother has nothing to give him but river water, so he is crying. Swallow, Swallow, little Swallow, will you not bring her the ruby out of my sword-hilt? My feet are fastened to this pedestal and I cannot move."

"I am waited for in Egypt," said the Swallow. "My friends are flying up and down the Nile, and talking to the large lotus-flowers. Soon they will go to sleep in the tomb of the great King. The King is there himself in his painted coffin. He is wrapped in yellow linen, and embalmed with spices. Round his neck is a chain of pale green jade, and his hands are like withered leaves."

"Swallow, Swallow, little Swallow," said the Prince, "will you not stay with me for one night, and be my messenger? The boy is so thirsty, and the mother so sad."

"I don't think I like boys," answered the Swallow. "Last summer, when I was staying on the river, there were two rude boys, the miller's sons, who were always throwing stones at me. They never hit me, of course; we swallows fly far too well for that, and besides, I come of a family famous for its agility; but still, it was a mark of disrespect."

But the Happy Prince looked so sad that the little Swallow was sorry. "It is very cold here," he said; "but I will stay with you for one night, and be your messenger."

"Thank you, little Swallow," said the Prince.

So the Swallow picked out the great ruby from the Prince's sword, and flew away with it in his beak over the roofs of the town.

He passed by the cathedral tower, where the white marble angels were sculptured. He passed by the palace and heard the sound of dancing. A beautiful girl came out on the balcony with her lover. "How wonderful the stars are," he said to her, "and how wonderful is the power of love!"

"I hope my dress will be ready in time for the State-ball," she answered; "I have ordered passion-flowers to be embroidered on it; but the seamstresses are so lazy."

He passed over the river, and saw the lanterns hanging to the masts of the ships. He passed over the Ghetto, and saw the old Jews bargaining with each other, and weighing out money in copper scales. At last he came to the poor house and looked in. The boy was tossing feverishly on his bed, and the mother had fallen asleep, she was so tired. In he hopped, and laid the great ruby on the table beside the woman's thimble. Then he flew gently round the bed, fanning the boy's forehead with his wings. "How cool I feel!" said the boy, "I must be getting better"; and he sank into a delicious slumber.

Then the Swallow flew back to the Happy Prince, and told him what he had done. "It is curious," he remarked, "but I feel quite warm now, although it is so cold."

"That is because you have done a good action," said the Prince. And the little Swallow began to think, and then he fell asleep. Thinking always made him sleepy.

When day broke he flew down to the river and had a bath. "What a remarkable phenomenon!" said the Professor of Ornithology as he was passing over the bridge. "A swallow in winter!" And he wrote a long letter about it to the local newspaper. Every one quoted it, it was full of so many words that they could not understand.

"To-night I go to Egypt," said the Swallow, and he was in high spirits at the prospect. He visited all the public monuments, and sat a long time on top of the church steeple. Wherever he went the Sparrows chirruped, and said to each other, "What a distinguished stranger!" so he enjoyed himself very much.

When the moon rose he flew back to the Happy Prince. "Have you any commissions for Egypt?" he cried; "I am just starting."

"Swallow, Swallow, little Swallow," said the Prince, "will you not stay with me one night longer?"

"I am waited for in Egypt," answered the Swallow. "To-morrow my friends will fly up to the Second Cataract. The riverhorse couches there among the bulrushes, and on a great granite house sits the God Memnon. All night long he watches the stars, and when the morning star shines he utters one cry of joy, and then he is silent. At noon the yellow lions come down to the water's edge to drink. They have eyes like green beryls, and their roar is louder than the roar of the cataract."

"Swallow, Swallow, little Swallow," said the Prince, "far away across the city I see a young man in a garret. He is leaning over a desk covered with papers, and in a tumbler by his side there is a bunch of withered violets. His hair is brown and crisp, and his lips are red as a pomegranate, and he has large and dreamy eyes. He is trying to finish a play for the Director of the Theatre, but he is too cold to write any more. There is no fire in the grate, and hunger has made him faint."

"I will wait with you one night longer," said the Swallow, who really had a good heart. "Shall I take him another ruby?"

"Alas! I have no ruby now," said the Prince; "my eyes are all that I have left. They are made of rare sapphires, which were brought out of India a thousand years ago. Pluck out one of them and take it to him. He will sell it to the jeweller, and buy firewood, and finish his play."

"Dear Prince," said the Swallow, "I cannot do that"; and he began to weep.

"Swallow, Swallow, little Swallow," said the Prince, "do as I command you."

So the Swallow plucked out the Prince's eye, and flew away to the student's garret. It was easy enough to get in, as there was a hole in the roof. Through this he darted, and came into the room. The young man had his head buried in his hands, so he did not hear the flutter of the bird's wings, and when he looked up he found the beautiful sapphire lying on the withered violets.

"I am beginning to be appreciated," he cried; "this is from some great admirer. Now I can finish my play," and he looked quite happy.

The next day the Swallow flew down to the harbour. He sat on the mast of a large vessel and watched the sailors hauling big chests out of the hold with ropes. "Heave a-hoy!" they shouted as each chest came up. "I am going to Egypt!" cried the Swallow, but nobody minded, and when the moon rose he flew back to the Happy Prince.

"I am come to bid you good-bye," he cried.

"Swallow, Swallow, little Swallow," said the Prince, "will you not stay with me one night longer?"

"It is winter," answered the Swallow, "and the chill snow will soon be here. In Egypt the sun is warm on the green palm-trees, and the crocodiles lie in the mud and look lazily about them. My companions are building a nest in the Temple of Baalbec, and the pink and white doves are watching them, and cooing to each other. Dear Prince, I must leave you, but I will never forget you, and next spring I will bring you back two beautiful jewels in place of those you have given away. The ruby shall be redder than a red rose, and the sapphire shall be as blue as the great sea."

"In the square below," said the Happy Prince, "there stands a little match-girl. She has let her matches fall in the gutter, and they are all spoiled. Her father will beat her if she does not bring home some money, and she is crying. She has no shoes or stockings, and her little head is bare. Pluck out my other eye, and give it to her, and her father will not beat her."

"I will stay with you one night longer," said the Swallow, "but I cannot pluck out your eye. You would be quite blind then."

"Swallow, Swallow, little Swallow," said the Prince, "do as I command you."

So he plucked out the Prince's other eye, and darted down with it. He swooped past the match-girl, and slipped the jewel into the palm of her hand. "What a lovely bit of glass!" cried the little girl; and she ran home, laughing.

Then the Swallow came back to the Prince. "You are blind now," he said, "so I will stay with you always."

"No, little Swallow," said the poor prince, "you must go away to Egypt."

"I will stay with you always," said the Swallow, and he slept at the Prince's feet.

All the next day he sat on the Prince's shoulder, and told him stories of what he had seen in strange lands. He told him of the red ibises, who stand in long rows on the banks of the Nile, and catch goldfish in their beaks; of the Sphinx, who is as old as the world itself, and lives in the desert, and knows everything; of the merchants, who walk slowly by the side of their camels and carry amber beads in their hands; of the King of the Mountains of the Moon, who is as black as ebony, and worships a large crystal; of the great green snake that sleeps in a palm-tree, and has twenty priests to feed it with honey-cakes; and of the pygmies who sail over a big lake on large flat leaves, and are always at war with the butterflies.

"Dear little Swallow," said the Prince, "you tell me of marvellous things, but more marvellous than anything is the suffering of men and of women. There is no Mystery so great as Misery. Fly over my city, little Swallow, and tell me what you see there."

So the Swallow flew over the great city, and saw the rich making merry in their beautiful houses, while the beggars were sitting at the gates. He flew into dark lanes, and saw the white faces of starving children looking out listlessly at the black streets. Under the archway of a bridge two little boys were lying in one another's arms to try and keep themselves warm. "How hungry we are!" they said. "You must not lie here," shouted the watchman, and they wandered out into the rain.

Then he flew back and told the Prince what he had seen.

"I am covered with fine gold," said the Prince, "you must take it off, leaf by leaf, and give it to my poor; the living always think that gold can make them happy."

Leaf after leaf of the fine gold the Swallow picked off, till the Happy Prince looked quite dull and grey. Leaf after leaf of the fine gold he brought to the poor, and the children's faces grew rosier, and they laughed and played games in the street. "We have bread now!" they cried.

Then the snow came, and after the snow came the frost. The streets looked as if they were made of silver, they were so bright and glistening; long icicles like crystal daggers hung down from the eaves of the houses, everybody went about in furs, and the little boys wore scarlet caps and skated on the ice.

The poor little Swallow grew colder and colder, but he would not leave the Prince, he loved him too well. He picked up crumbs outside the baker's door when the baker was not looking, and tried to keep himself warm by flapping his wings.

But at last he knew that he was going to die. He had just enough strength to fly up to the Prince's shoulder once more. "Good-bye, dear Prince!" he murmured, "will you let me kiss your hand?"

"I am glad that you are going to Egypt at last, little Swallow," said the Prince, "you have stayed too long here; but you must kiss me on the lips, for I love you."

"It is not to Egypt that I am going," said the Swallow. "I am going to the House of Death. Death is the brother of Sleep, is he not?"

And he kissed the Happy Prince on the lips, and fell down dead at his feet.

At that moment a curious crack sounded inside the statue, as if something had broken. The fact is that the leaden heart had snapped right in two. It certainly was a dreadfully hard frost.

Early the next morning the Mayor was walking in the square

below in company with the Town Councillors. As they passed the column he looked up at the statue: "Dear me! how shabby the Happy Prince looks!" he cried.

"How shabby, indeed!" cried the Town Councillors, who always agreed with the Mayor; and they went up to look at it.

"The ruby has fallen out of his sword, his eyes are gone, and he is golden no longer," said the Mayor; "in fact, he is little better than a beggar!"

"Little better than a beggar," said the Town Councillors.

"And here is actually a dead bird at his feet!" continued the Mayor. "We must really issue a proclamation that birds are not to be allowed to die here." And the Town Clerk made a note of the suggestion.

So they pulled down the statue of the Happy Prince. "As he is no longer beautiful he is no longer useful," said the Art Professor at the University.

Then they melted the statue in a furnace, and the Mayor held a meeting of the Corporation to decide what was to be done with the metal. "We must make another statue, of course," he said, "and it shall be a statue of myself."

"Of myself," said each of the Town Councillors, and they quarrelled. When I last heard of them they were quarrelling still.

"What a strange thing!" said the overseer of the workmen at the foundry. "This broken lead heart will not melt in the furnace. We must throw it away." So they threw it on a dust-heap where the dead Swallow was also lying.

"Bring me the two most precious things in the city," said God to one of His Angels; and the Angel brought Him the leaden heart and the dead bird.

"You have rightly chosen," said God, "for in my garden of Paradise this little bird shall sing for evermore, and in my city of gold the Happy Prince shall praise me."

Brian's Skates

by
W.O. MITCHELL
(1914–   )

W.O. Mitchell's Who Has Seen the Wind *has long been a
favourite of Prairie life, told against the immeasurable sweep of
the Saskatchewan skyline. "Brian's Skates" is one of the many
memorable episodes of Mitchell's much-loved novel: the story of
a boy's poignant Christmas hopes, and of his quiet disappointment when they fail to materialize.*

I n the O'Connal family, Christmas began as a rule early in December, when the boys started to decide what presents they would like. In Brian's second year of school, Christmas was called earlier to the parents' attention because with the beginning of winter Brian asked for skates.

Maggie's first response was unbelief; it was difficult for her to think that one of her boys was old enough to want skates. She reminded him that he was just past seven and that Forbsie Hoffman did not have skates yet. Brian replied that Art Sherry had them. Art, who was a year and a half older than Brian, had inherited a pair from an older sister; their high tops had been cut down; they had to be worn with three pairs of woolen socks so that Art's feet would not slide around in the shoes—but to Brian, skateless, they were things whose beauty would endure forever.

Skates became a frequent topic of conversation at meals. At length the grandmother said she was sick of hearing about them; would it not be possible to get the child a pair so that he could break his neck and give them a few peaceful meals? Maggie forbade Brian to mention skates at the table again.

The day that he saw the new tube skates in the hardware store window, Brian called on his father at work.

"Why can't I have them, Dad?"

"Because your mother says you're too young for them."

"But I'm not—I'm—"

"Seven's pretty young for skates."

"I was seven a long time ago—in the fall—I'm past seven!"

"You're still too young—when you're older—next year, per-haps."

"I'll be older at Christmas. That's a long ways away. May I have them for Christmas?"

"I don't think so, Spalpeen."

After Brian had left, Gerald felt a pang of remorse; it was diffi-cult to see why the boy could not have skates. That night he had a talk with Maggie.

"Perhaps by Christmas time?" he asked her. "He'll be almost seven and a half then."

His wife looked at him a long time before answering him. "You know—I love him too, Gerald. I hate to deny them things as much as you. It's just that he seems so—do you think he's old enough? Do you—honestly?"

"I think so, Maggie."

"It isn't because he wants them so badly?"

"Well—he's old enough—let him skate."

After a decent interval Brian was told that he might possibly get skates for Christmas. Bobbie then insisted that he should get skates too, but he finally settled for a hockey stick and a puck.

Brian looked forward with eagerness to the promised skates. He thought of them often—during school hours—whenever the boys gathered after school with worn, sliver-thin sticks to play a sort of hockey between tin-can goal posts and with a blob of frozen horse manure for a puck. The more he thought of them, the less envious he was of Art with his "wimmen skates." There would be nothing feminine about *his*; they would be sturdy tubes with thick, felt tongues.

The night before Christmas he was almost sick with excite-ment and anticipation as he lay in his bed with Bobbie beside him. He could see the skates clearly with their frosted tubing and the clear runners that would cling to his thumb when he ran it along them to test their sharpness. He could see himself gliding over the river, alone on shining ice. With a twist and a lean—a shower of ice-snow—he came to a breath-taking stop.

Bobbie stirred in his sleep.

"You awake, Bobbie?"

Bobbie did not answer him.

Perhaps there would be straps over the ankles; not that he would need them, for his ankles were strong. His feet wouldn't slop. He flexed them beneath the covers—stronger than anything. Maybe they were too strong, and when he pushed, he would push the ice clean full of cracks.

He closed his eyes tightly. If only he could get to sleep the time would pass more quickly. When one slept it was nothing—swift as a person on skates—swift as the wind…

"He came, Brian! He came!"

Bobbie was jumping on the bed, his hair bright in the winter sunshine that filled the room.

Brian jumped from the bed. "C'mon!"

Their stockings, lumpy with oranges, each with a colored cardboard clown protruding from its top, hung from the mantel of the fireplace. Bobbie's sleigh that could be steered was before the tree. Bobbie threw himself upon the parcels.

"Wait a minute!" cried Brian. "They're not all yours—just with your name!"

He began to sort out the presents upon which Maggie the night before had printed in the large block letters that Brian could easily read.

Anxiously Brian watched the growing pile of parcels beside him. He opened a deep box to find it full of colored cars and an engine, in little compartments. He opened another—a mechanical affair which when wound caused two long black men to dance, all the while turning around. Slippers were in one promising-looking parcel. As he opened the last of his parcels he was filled with the horrible conviction that something was wrong.

Then he saw a parcel behind the Christmas tree. His name was on it. He opened it. They were not tube skates; they were not single-runnered skates; they were bob-skates, double-runnered affairs with curving toe-cleats and a half-bucket arrangement to catch the heel of the shoe.

For a swift moment Brian's heart was filled with mixed feeling; disappointment bitter and blinding was there, but with it a half-dazed feeling of inner release and relief that he had got skates. They were skates, he told himself as he turned them over in his hands.

"What's the matter, Brian?" Bobbie had looked up from his fire engine.

Brian got up and went into the living room; he sat on the window seat next to the shamrock plant, the bob-skates upon his knees. When Bobbie came through a while later clutching a hockey stick a foot longer than himself, Brian paid no attention to him.

Throughout dinner he spoke only when spoken to. When his father and uncle were seated in the living room with lighted cigars and his mother and grandmother were in the kitchen, washing the dinner dishes, he went unnoticed to the hallway, put on his coat and toque, and with the bob-skates went out.

He passed other children as he walked, pulling Christmas sleighs and Christmas toboggans, some with gleaming Christmas skates slung over their shoulders. Through the fiercely tinseled snow sparkling unbearably in the sunlight he walked, not toward the downtown bridge where children and adults swooped over cleared ice, but toward the powerhouse and the small footbridge. There he sat near a clump of willow, fitted the skates to his feet, buckled the straps over his insteps, and went knee-deep through the snow on the riverbank to the ice.

Once on the ice he stood for a moment on trembling legs. He pushed with one foot; it skidded sideways; the other went suddenly from under him, and he came down with a bump that snatched his breath. He got carefully up and stood uncertainly. He pushed a tentative skate ahead, then another. He stood still with knees half-bent. He gave a push with one skate preparatory to swooping over the ice. He fell flat on his face. He got up.

He began a slow forward sliding across the ice—painfully—noncommittal steps of a stroke victim just risen from bed. He was not skating, he was walking with an overwhelming feeling of frustration that reminded him of dreams in which he ran with all his might, but stayed only in one spot. He fell again, and felt his elbow go numb. He sat on the ice, looking at his own feet ahead of him.

He began to cry.

Brian's parents, his grandmother, and his uncle were seated in the living room when he got back to the house. He was carrying the bob-skates as he came out of the hallway.

"Been skatin'?" asked Sean.

Brian did not answer him. "Uncle Sean asked you a question, Son," said Maggie.

Sean's big, freckled hand reached out to take one of the bob-skates. "Damn fool question," said Sean. "Fella doesn't skate with bob-skates. Had somebody pullin' you, did you?"

Brian shook his head.

"What's wrong, Spalpeen?" Brian's father was looking at his tear-stained face.

Brian rushed from the room.

"What do you mean?" Maggie turned to Sean. "What's wrong with his skates? What did you mean—"

"They call 'em skates," said Sean. "Can't skate with 'em. Just teaches kids a healthy respect fer ice, that's all. Got no grip at all—skid like hell. Never forget the first time I took Gerald on ice with a pair—'bout the same age as Brian. He had one hell of a time—ended up hangin' onto me coattails whilst I pulled him around."

"But—then that means that Brian—he's—" Maggie got up and went swiftly from the room.

She found Brian at the kitchen window.

"Don't they work, Son?"

Still looking out the window, Brian shook his head.

"Aren't they what you wanted?"

"Tubes," he got out with difficulty. "Like in Harris's."

"I'm sorry, Brian." Maggie watched his shoulders moving. She turned his face around to her. "Don't—please don't! I'll fix it!"

She went to the phone.

"Mr. Harris? Have you a pair of—of tube skates left? Small size? I wonder if we—if you could come down to the store with me—my son—will you—will—"

"Mother!"

That night Maggie O'Connal stood at her children's bedside. With her white nightgown almost to her heels, her hair in two black braids, she looked like a little girl in the dimness of the room.

A glinting caught her eye, and she saw a length of leather lace hanging down the side of the bed. Brian slept with his hand clenched around the runner of one tube skate, his nose almost inside the boot. Maggie reached out one hand and laid it lightly upon Brian's cheek; she kept it there for a long time. Then she gently took the skate from his hand.

She turned and with the flat, soft steps of the barefooted went from the room.

In Calabria

by
NIKOS KAZANTZAKIS
(1883–1957)

Nikos Kazantzakis is perhaps best known for the film adaptations of his novels, The Last Temptation of Christ *and* Zorba the Greek. *"In Calabria" is a beautiful little parable-like story of the proverbial stranger at the door—a theme that is so much a part of the Christmas tradition. A quiet little story of quite human proportions: of generosity, understanding and basic human needs.*

It was almost nightfall. The whole day: rain, torrents of rain. Drenched to the bone, I arrived in a little Calabrian village. I had to find a hearth where I could dry out, a corner where I could sleep. The streets were deserted, the doors bolted. The dogs were the only ones to scent the stranger's breath; they began to bark from within the court-yards. The peasants in this region are wild and misanthropic, suspicious of strangers. I hesitated at every door, extended my hand, but did not dare to knock.

O for my late grandfather in Crete who took his lantern each evening and made the rounds of the village to see if any stranger had come. He would take him home, feed him, give him a bed for the night, and then in the morning see him off with a cup of wine and a slice of bread. Here in the Calabrian villages there were no such grandfathers.

Suddenly I saw an open door at the edge of the village. Inclining my head, I looked in: a murky corridor with a lighted fire at the far end and an old lady bent over it. She seemed to be cooking. Not a sound, nothing but the burning wood. It was fragrant; it must have been pine. I crossed the threshold and entered, bumping against a long table which stood in the mid-dle of the room. Finally I reached the fire and sat down on a stool which I found in front of the hearth. The old lady was squatting on another stool, stirring the meal with a wooden spoon. I felt that she eyed me rapidly, without turning. But she said nothing. Taking off my jacket, I began to dry it. I sensed happiness rising in me like warmth, from my feet to my shins, my thighs, my breast. Hungrily, avidly, I inhaled the fragrance of the steam rising from the pot. The meal must have been baked beans; the aroma was overwhelming. Once more I realized to what an extent earthly happiness is made to the measure of man. It is not a rare bird which we must pursue at one moment in heaven, at the next in our minds. Happiness is a domestic bird found in our own courtyards.

Rising, the old lady took down two soup plates from a shelf next to her. She filled them, and the whole world smelled of beans. Lighting a lamp, she placed it on the long table. Next she brought two wooden spoons and a loaf of black bread. We sat down opposite each other. She made the sign of the cross, then glanced rapidly at me. I understood. I crossed myself and we began to eat. We were both hungry; we did not breathe a word. I had decided not to speak in order to see what would happen. Could she be a mute, I asked myself—or perhaps she's mad, one of those peaceful, kindly lunatics so much like saints.

As soon as we finished, she prepared a bed for me on a bench to the right of the table. I lay down, and she lay down on the other bench opposite me. Outside the rain was falling by the bucketful. For a considerable time I heard the water cackle on the roof, mixed with the old lady's calm, quiet breathing. She must have been tired, for she fell asleep the moment she inclined her head. Little by little, with the rain and the old lady's rhythmical respiration, I too slipped into sleep. When I awoke, I saw daylight peering through the cracks in the door.

The old lady had already risen and placed a saucepan on the fire to prepare the morning milk. I looked at her now in the sparse daylight. Shriveled and humped, she could fit into the palm of your hand. Her legs were so swollen that she had to stop at every step and catch her breath. But her eyes, only her large, pitch-black eyes, gleamed with youthful, unaging brilliance. How beautiful she must have been in her youth, I thought to myself, cursing man's fate, his inevitable deterioration. Sitting down opposite each other again, we drank the milk. Then I rose and slung my carpetbag over my shoulder.

I took out my wallet, but the old lady colored deeply.

"No, no," she murmured, extending her hand.

As I looked at her in astonishment, the whole of her bewrinkled face suddenly gleamed.

"Goodbye, and God bless you," she said. "May the Lord repay you for the good you've done me. Since my husband died I've never slept so well."

The *Story* of the *Christmas Stocking*

by

ELIZABETH WETHERELL *and* AMY LOTHROP
(1819–1885)   (1827–1915)

A listener from New Glasgow, Nova Scotia recently sent me a little book called Carl Krinken, adding that it reminded her of the Fireside Al Christmas readings. The authors, it turns out, were Susan Bogert Warner and Anna Bartlett Warner, two sisters who wrote under the pseudonyms of Elizabeth Wetherell and Amy Lothrop. This little book, from which "The Story of the Christmas Stocking" has been taken, was first published in 1855, and remained popular throughout the decade, but has not been reprinted since then so far as I can see. It's a little Christmas jewel, glazed over with the appropriate coating of Victorian sentiment, and I would very much like to thank Penny McMullin of New Glasgow for her kindness in sending the book to me.

Carl Krinken is a little boy who has a series of conversations with different objects: a penny, a purse, two shoes, a pine cone. The final story is Carl's conversation with a Christmas stocking.

"**I**t's too bad!" said Carl. "I've heard six stories and a little piece, and now there's nothing left but this old stocking!"

"I believe I will not tell you my story at all," said the stocking.

"But you shall," said Carl, "or else I will cut you all up into little pieces."

"Then, you certainly will never hear it," said the stocking.

"Well, now," said Carl, "what a disagreeable old stocking you are. Why don't you begin at once?"

"I am tired of always being at the foot," said the stocking; "as one may say, at the fag end. And besides, your way of speaking is not proper. I suppose you have been told as much before. This is not the way little boys used to speak when *I* was knit."

"You are only a stocking," said Carl.

"Everything that is worth speaking to at all, is worth speaking to politely," replied the stocking.

"I can't help it," said Carl, "you might tell me your story, then. I'm sure one of my own red stockings would tell its story in a minute."

"Yes," said the gray stocking; "and the story would be 'Lived on little Carl's foot all my life, and never saw anything.'"

"It wouldn't be true, then," said Carl, "for I never wear them except on Sundays. Mother says she can't afford it."

"Nobody afforded it once," said the stocking. "My ancestors were not heard of until ten or eleven hundred years ago, and then they were made of leather or linen. And then people wore cloth hose; and then, some time in the sixteenth century, silk stockings made their appearance in England. But there was never a pair of knit woollen stockings until the year 1564."

"I say," said Carl, "do stop—will you? and go on with your story." And putting his hand down into the old stocking, he stretched it out as far as he could on his little fingers.

"You'd better amuse yourself in some other way," said the stocking. "If my yarn should break, it will be the worse for your story."

"Well, why don't you begin, then?" said Carl, laying him down again.

"It's not always pleasant to recount one's misfortunes," said the stocking, "and I have come down in the world sadly. You would hardly think it, I dare say, but I did once belong to a very good family."

"So you do now," said Carl. "There never was anybody in the world better than my mother; and father's very good too."

"Yes," said the stocking again, "Mrs. Krinken does seem to be quite a respectable woman for her station in life, very neat about her house, and I presume makes most excellent porridge. But you see, where I used to live, porridge had never even been heard of. I declare," said the stocking, "I can hardly believe it myself, I think my senses are getting blunted. I have lain in that chest so long with a string of red onions, that I have really almost forgotten what musk smells like! But my lady Darlington always fainted away if anybody mentioned onions, so of course the old squire never had them on the dinner table even. A fine old gentleman he was; not very tall, but as straight almost as ever; and with ruddy cheeks, and hair that was not white but silver colour. His hand shook a little sometimes, but his heart never—and his voice was as clear as a whistle. His step went cheerfully about the house and grounds, although it was only to the music of his walking-stick; and music that was, truly, to all the poor of the neighbourhood. His stick was like him. He would have neither gold nor silver head to it, but it was all of good English oak, the top finely carved into a supposed likeness of Edward the Confessor.

"As for my lady, she was all stateliness, very beautiful too, or had been; and the sound of her dress was like the wings of a wild bird."

"I think I shall like to hear this story," said Carl, setting himself on his box and patting his hands together once or twice.

"I dare say you will," said the stocking, "when I tell it to you. However—Well—

"A great many years ago it was Christmas Eve at Squire Darlington's, and the squire sat alone in his wide hall. Every window was festooned with ivy leaves and holly, which twisted about the old carving, and drooped, and hung round the silver sconces, and thence downward towards the floor. The silver hands of the sconces held tall wax candles, but they were not lit. The picture frames wore wreaths, from which the old portraits looked out gloomily enough, not finding the adornment so becoming as they had done a century or so before; and even the squire's high-backed chair was crowned with a bunch of holly berry. There was no danger of their being in his way, for he rarely leaned back in his chair, but sat up quite straight, with one hand on his knee and the other on the arm of his chair. On that particular evening his hand rested on me; for I and my companion stocking had been put on for the first time."

"I don't see how he could get his hand on his stocking," said Carl, "if he sat up. Look—I couldn't touch mine."

"You needn't try to tell me anything about stockings," replied that article of dress, somewhat contemptuously. "I know their limits as well as most people. But in those days, Master Carl, gentlemen wore what they called small-clothes—very different from your new-fangled pantaloons."

"I don't wear pantaloons," said Carl; "I wear trousers." But the stocking did not heed the interruption.

"The small-clothes reached only to the knee—a little above or a little below—and so met the long stockings half way. Some people wore very fanciful stockings, of different colours, and embroidered; but Squire Darlington's were always of gray woollen yarn, very fine and soft, as you see I am, and tied above the knee with black ribbons; and his shoes were always black, with large black bows and silver buckles.

"He sat there alone in the wide hall, with one hand on me, and his eyes fixed upon the fire, waiting for the arrival of the Yule Log. For in those days, the night before Yule or Christmas, the chief fire in the house was built with an immense log, which was cut and brought in with great rejoicing and ceremony, and lighted with a brand saved from the log of last year. All the servants in the house had gone out to help to roll the log and swell the noise, and the fire of the day had burnt down to a mere bed of coals; and the hall was so still you could almost hear the ivy leaves rustle on the old wall outside. I don't know but the Squire did."

"What did he stay there for?" said Carl. "Was he thinking?"

"He might have been," said the stocking—"indeed I rather think he was, for he stroked and patted me two or three times. Or he might have been listening to the wind singing its Christmas song."

"Can the wind sing?" said Carl.

"Ay, and sigh too. Most of all about the time of other people's holidays. It's a wild, sighing kind of a song at best—whistled, and sung, and sighed together—sometimes round the house, and sometimes through a keyhole. I heard what it said that night, well enough. You won't understand it, but this was it:—

> "'Christmas again!—Christmas again!
>   With its holly berries so bright and red;
>   They gleam in the wood, they grow by the lane:
>   Oh, hath not Christmas a joyful tread?
>
> "'Christmas again! Christmas again!
>   What does it find? and what does it bring?
>   And what does it miss, that should remain?
>   Oh! Christmas time is a wonderful thing.
>
> "'Christmas again! Christmas again!
>   There are bright green leaves on the holly tree;
>   But withered leaves fly over the plain,
>   And the forests are brown and bare to see.
>
> "'Christmas again! Christmas again!
>   The snow lies light, and the wind is cold;

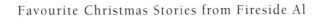

But the wind—it reacheth some hearts of pain,
And the snow—it falleth on heads grown old.

"'Christmas again! Christmas again!
What kindling fires flash through the hall!
The flames may flash, but the shadows remain;
And where do the shadows this night fall?

"'Christmas again! Christmas again!
It looks through the windows—it treads the floor;
Seeking for what earth could not retain—
Watching for those who will come no more.

"'Christmas again! Christmas again!
Why doth not the pride of the house appear?
Where is the sound of her silken train?
And that empty chair—what doeth it here?

"'Christmas again! Christmas again!
With hearts as light as ever did bound;
And feet as pretty as ever were fain
To tread a measure the hall around.

"'Christmas again! Christmas again!—
O thoughts, be silent! Who called for ye?
Must Christmas time be a time of pain,
Because of the loved, from pain set free?

"'Christmas again! Christmas again!
Once Christmas and joy came hand in hand;
The hall may its holiday look regain,—
But the empty chairs must empty stand.'

"The wind took much less time to sing the song than I have
taken to tell it," said the stocking; "a low sigh round the house,
and a whistle or two, told all. Then suddenly a door at the lower
end of the hall flew open, and a boy sprang in, exclaiming—
'Grandfather, it's coming!'

He was dressed just after the fashion of the old Squire, only with delicate white stockings and black velvet small-clothes; while his long-flapped waistcoat was gaily flowered, and his shoes had crimson rosettes. And almost as he spoke, a side door opened, and my lady glided in, her dress rustling softly as she came; while the wind rushed in after her, and tossed and waved the feathers in her tall head-dress.

There was heard a distant murmur of shouts and laughter, and young Edric clapped his hands and then stood still to listen; and presently, the whole troop of servants poured into the hall, from that same door at the lower end. All were dressed in the best and gayest clothes they had; the women wore ivy wreaths, and the men carried sprigs of holly at their button-holes. First came a number bearing torches; then many others, rolling, and pulling, and pushing the great log, on which one of the men-servants, whimsically dressed, was endeavouring to keep his seat; while every other man, woman, and child, about the place, crowded in after.

Then the log was rolled into the great fire-place, and duly lighted; and everybody clapped hands and rejoiced in its red glow, and Master Edric shouted as loud as the rest.

"Edric," said my lady, when the hall was quiet once more, though not empty, for all the household were to spend Christmas Eve there together—"Edric, go take a partner, and dance us a minuet."

And Edric walked round the hall till he came to little May Underwood, the forester's daughter; and then bringing the white stockings and the crimson rosettes close side by side together, and making her a low bow, he took her hand and led her out upon the polished floor.

The Yule Log was in a full blaze now, and the light shone from end to end of the hall; falling upon the bright floor and the long row of servants and retainers that were arranged around, and glossily reflected from the sharp holly leaves and its bright red berries. The old portraits did not light up much, and looked very near as gloomy as ever; but a full halo of the firelight was about the squire's chair, and upon my lady as she stood beside him. Two or three of the serving-men played a strange old tune upon as strange old instruments; and the forester now and then threw in a few wild notes of his bugle, that sounded through the house and aroused all the echoes; but the wind sighed outside still.

And all this while the little dancers were going through the slow, graceful steps of their pretty dance; with the most respectful bows and courtesies, the most ceremonious presenting of hands and acceptance of the same, the most graceful and complicated turns and bends; till at last when the music suddenly struck into a quick measure, Edric presented his right hand to little May, and they danced gaily forward to where my lady stood near the squire, and made their low reverence—first to her, and then to each other. Then Edric led his little partner back to her seat, and returned to his grandmother. For my lady was his grandmother, and he had no parents.

As the Yule Log snapped and crackled and blazed higher and higher, even so did the mirth of all in the great hall. They talked, and laughed, and sang, and played games, and not an echo in the house could get leave to be silent.

All of a sudden, in the midst of the fun, a little boy dressed like Robin Redbreast in a dark coat and bright red waistcoat, opened one of the hall doors; and just showing himself for a moment, he flung the door clear back and an old man entered. His hair was perfectly white, and so was his beard, which reached down to his waist. On his head was a crown of yew and ivy, and in his hand a long staff topped with holly berries; his dress was a long brown robe which fell down about his feet, and on it were sewed little spots of white cloth to represent snow. He made a low bow to the squire and my lady, and when Robin Redbreast had discreetly closed the door so far that but a little wind could come in, he began to sing in a queer little cracked voice—

> "Oh! here come I, old Father Christmas, welcome or not.
> I hope old Father Christmas will never be forgot.
>   Make room, room, I say,
> That I may lead Mince Pye this way,
> Walk in, Mince Pye, and act thy part,
> And show the gentles thy valiant heart."

With that Robin opened the door again, and another figure

came in, dressed like a woman in a dark purple gown bordered with a light brownish yellow. A large apple was fastened on top of her head, and she wore bunches of raisins at her ears instead of earrings; while her necklace was of large pieces of citron strung together, and her bracelets of cloves, and alspice, and cinnamon. In her hand she carried a large wooden sword."

"What was that for?" said Carl, who had listened with the most intense interest.

"Why to fight off the people that wanted to make her up into real mince pie, I suppose," said the stocking. "She came into the room singing.—

"'Room, room, you gallant souls, give me room to rhyme,
  I will show you some festivity this Christmas time.
  Bring me the man that bids me stand,
  Who says he'll cut me down with an audacious hand.
  I'll cut him and hew him as small as a fly,
  And see what he'll do then to make his mince pye.
                    Walk in, St. George.'

"'Oh! in come I St. George, the man of courage bold,
  With my sword and buckler I have won three crowns of gold;
  I fought the fiery Dragon, and brought him to the slaughter,
  I saved a beauteous Queen and a King of England's daughter.
  If thy mind is high, my mind is bold;
  If thy blood is hot, I will make it cold.'"

"What did he want to do that for?" said Carl.

"Oh, in the days when St. George lived," replied the stocking, "the more men a man killed the more people thought of him; and this man was trying to make himself like St. George. He had a great pasteboard helmet on his head, with a long peacock's feather streaming from the top of it, and a wooden sword, and a tin-covered shield on which were nailed clusters of holly berries in the figure of a cross. His shoes were of wood too, and his jacket and small-clothes of buckskin, with sprigs of yew fastened upon all the seams, and great knots of green and red ribbons at the knees. As soon as he had sung his song he began his fight with Mince Pye, and a dreadful fight it was, if one might judge by the noise; also Mince Pye's sword became quite red with the holly berries. But St. George let his shield take all the blows, and when Mince Pye had spent all her strength upon it, he thrust at her with his sword and down she came."

"Who? Mince Pye?" said Carl. "Oh that's too bad!"

"Mince Pye thought so too," said the stocking, "for she cried out,

> 'Oh, St. George, spare my life!'

Then said old Father Christmas,

> 'Is no Doctor to be found
> To cure Mince Pye who is bleeding on the ground?'"

"Was there any?" said Carl.

"There was somebody who called himself one. He came running right into the hall the minute old Father Christmas called for him, and you never saw such a queer little figure. He had an old black robe, and a black cap on his head, and a black patch over one eye."

"What was that for?" said Carl.

"He'd been curing himself, I suppose," said the stocking. "And it would seem that he wasn't satisfied with any of his features, for he had put on a long pasteboard nose painted red, and a pasteboard chin. In his hand he carried a great basket of bottles. If one might believe his own account, he was a doctor worth having.

> "Oh yes, there is a doctor to be found
> To cure Mince Pye who is bleeding on the ground.
> I cure the sick of every pain,
> And none of them ever are sick again."

Father Christmas thought it must cost a good deal to be cured after that fashion, so like a prudent man he said,

> "Doctor, what is thy fee?"

And the Doctor probably didn't like to be questioned for he answered,

> "Ten pounds is my fee;
>   But fifteen I must take of thee
>   Before I set this gallant free."

But as it was necessary that Mince Pye should be cured Father Christmas only said,

> "Work thy will, Doctor."

Then the Doctor took a bottle out of his basket and began to dance and sing round Mince Pye.

> "I have a little bottle by my side,
>   The fame of which spreads far and wide;
>   Drop a drop on this poor man's nose."

And with that Mince Pye jumped up as well as ever."

"But that wasn't all?" said Carl. "What else?"

"That was not quite all," said the stocking, "for another man came in, with a great basket of dolls at his back and a tall red cap on his head. And he sang too.

> "Oh! in come I, little saucy Jack,
>   With all my family at my back;
>   Christmas comes but once a year,
>   And when it does it brings good cheer,
>   Roast beef, plum pudding, and Mince Pye,
>   Who likes that any better than I;
>   Christmas makes us dance and sing;
>   Money in the purse is a very fine thing,
>   Ladies and gentlemen, give us what you please."

Then Squire Darlington and my lady each took out some money, and Edric carried it to the masquers, and as he hadn't any money himself he told them that he was very much obliged to them; and then they went off."

"What did they give them money for?" said Carl.

"Oh, they expected it—that was what they came for. People used to go about in that way to the rich houses at Christmas time, to get a little money by amusing the gentlefolks."

"I suppose they were very much amused," said Carl with a little sigh.

Very much—especially Edric. And after they were gone he came and stood before the great fire and thought it all over, smiling to himself with pleasure.

"Edric," said my lady, "it is time for you to go to bed."

"Yes grandmother—but I'm afraid I can't go to sleep."

"Why not?" said Squire Darlington. "What are you smiling at?"

"Oh, we've had such a splendid night, grandfather!—the people were dressed so finely—and didn't Mince Pye fight well? and wasn't the Doctor queer! And I'm sure my stocking will be as full as *anything*!"

Squire Darlington drew the boy towards him and seated him on his knee while he spoke thus; and passing his hand caressingly over the young joyous head, and smoothing the brown hair that was parted—child-fashion—in the middle of the forehead, and came curling down upon the lace frill; he looked into Edric's face with a world of pleasure and interest.

"And so you've enjoyed the evening, dear boy?" he said.

"O yes! grandfather—so much! I'm sure Christmas is the very happiest time of the whole year!"

Squire Darlington stroked down the hair again, and looked in the bright eyes, but with something of wistfulness now; and without stirring his hand from the boy's head, his look went towards the fire.

The Yule Log was blazing there steadily, although it now showed a great front of glowing coals that yet had not fallen from their place. A clear red heat was all that part of the log, and hardly to be distinguished from the bed of coals below; while bright points of flame curled and danced and ran scampering up the chimney, as if they too were playing Christmas games. But each end of the log yet held out against the fire, and had not even lost its native brown.

The Squire looked there with an earnest gaze that was not daunted by the glowing light; but his brows were slightly raised, and though the caressing movement of his hand was repeated, it seemed now to keep time to sorrowful music; and his lips had met on that boundary line between smiles and tears. Presently a little hand was laid against his cheek, and a little lace ruffle brushed lightly over its furrows.

"Grandfather, what's the matter? What makes you look grave?"

The Squire looked at him, and taking his hand in his own patted it softly against his face.

"The matter? my dear," he said. "Why the matter is that Christmas has come and gone a great many times."

"But that's good, grandfather," said Edric, clapping his hands together. "Just think! there'll be another Christmas in a year. Only a year. And we had one only a year ago—and such a pleasant Christmas!"

"Only a year," repeated the old man slowly. "No Edric, it is only sixty years."

"What do you mean, grandfather?" said the boy softly.

"Sixty years ago, my dear," said Squire Darlington, "there was just such a Yule Log as that, burning in this very fireplace. And the windows, and the picture-frames—there were not quite so many then—were trimmed with holly berries and yew from the same trees from which these wreaths have come to-day. And this old chair stood here, and everything in this old hall looked just as it does now."

"Well, grandfather?" said Edric catching his breath a little,—and the wind gave one of its low sighs through the keyhole.

"Well my dear—instead of one dear little couple on the floor"—and the old man drew the boy closer to him—"there were six,—as merry-eyed and light-footed little beings as ever trod this green earth. At the head I stood with your grandmother, Edric—a dear little thing she was!" said Squire Darlington with a kindly look towards my lady, whose eyes were cast down now, for a wonder, and her lips trembling a little. "Her two brothers, and my two, and the orphan boy that we loved like a brother; his sister, and my four little sisters—precious children! that they were—made up the rest. Light feet, and soft voices, and sweet laughter—they went through this old hall—like a troop of fairies, I was going to say,—more like a ray of pure human happiness.

"My father sat here, and my mother opposite; her picture watches the very spot now; and of these good friends at the other end of the hall—ay, old Cuthbert remembers it—there were two or three; but many others that bore their names.

"My child—that is sixty years ago!"

"And where are they now, grandfather?" said Edric, under his breath.

"In heaven—the most of them," said the old man, solemnly. "But one couple remains of the six. Of those other dear children not one is left—and not one but gave good hope in his death that he was going to be with Jesus. They remember yet that he came to earth, but they sing another song from ours—their hearts dance with a different joy. We shall know, one day, if we are faithful. They are exceeding fair to my remembrance, they are fairer now in reality."

The old squire was silent for a few minutes, with his eyes again turned towards the fire, while Edric looked up at the sweet portrait to which his grandfather had referred and wondered how it was that those eyes always met his. Then Squire Darlington spoke again, and with a different manner.

"Everybody that has money makes Christmas a time of feasting and rejoicing, Edric," he said. "What does Christmas-day celebrate?"

"The birth of Christ," said Edric, gravely.

"Yes!" said Squire Darlington. "The birth of Christ. 'Who, though he was rich, yet for our sakes became poor; that we through his poverty might be made rich.' There is a motto for Christmas-day! ay, for one's whole life."

"Grandfather," said Edric, "does everybody that loves Christ love all the poor disagreeable people?"

"This is what the Bible says, Edric. 'For if any man seeth that his brother have need, and shutteth up his bowels of compassion from him, how dwelleth the love of Christ in him?'"

"Grandfather," said Edric, thoughtfully, "when I am a man, I will take a great deal of care of poor people."

It was rather a sad smile that the old Squire gave him, and yet it was very tender.

"My dear Edric," he said, "never say, *when I am a man* I will do good. There is hardly any good work that a child may not help forward or help to keep back. Will you wait till you are a man, Edric, before you begin to love Christ?"

"I think I do love him now, grandfather," said Edric. "I should think everybody would; he has done so much for us."

There was the same look of love and sadness for a moment in the old man's face before he answered.

"My motto has another bearing, dear boy, which should be first in the heart of every man and every child, in this world, which Christ died to save—'*If ye love me*, keep my commandments.'"

And when the Christmas Eve was almost ended, Squire Darlington kissed and blessed his little grandson, and Edric went up-stairs to bed.

And the wind sighed no more that night."

"And did he do as he said he would, when he got to be a man?" inquired Carl.

"I don't know," said the stocking—"I never heard."

Christmas

by
GILLIAN FERNS
(1941–   )

A pause for a little poem by Gillian Ferns. A quiet moment by the Christmas fire.

Christmas

Wind blow,
sing low
for our darling
born this morning.

Life's new spring,
peace will bring
and joy to move
men's hearts to love.

A
Little Town
and a **Little Girl**

by
EMILY CARR
(1871–1945)

Emily Carr's childhood memories bring vividly to life the shops and streets of the then little town of Victoria at Christmas time—before the town became a city. Her painterly eye captures the scene in bold, colourful strokes, revealing in the little girl's perceptions the makings of this most remarkable woman.

Victoria Christmas weather was always nippy—generally there was snow. We sewed presents for weeks before Christmas came—kettle holders, needle books, penwipers and cross-stitch bookmarkers. Just before Christmas we went out into the woods, cut down a fir tree and brought it home so alive still that the warm house fooled it into thinking spring had come, and it breathed delicious live pine smell all over the house. We put fir and holly behind all the pictures and on the mantelpiece and everywhere.

Plum puddings were dangling from under the pantry shelf by the tails of their boiling cloths. A month ago we had all sat round the breakfast-room table, stoning raisins while someone read a story aloud. Everyone had given the pudding a good-luck stir before it went into the bowls and was tied down and boiled for hours in the copper wash boiler while spicy smells ran all over the house. On Christmas Day the biggest pudding came out for a final boil before being brought to the table with brandy fire leaping up its sides from the dish, and with a sprig of holly scorching and crackling on its top.

Christmas Eve Father took us into town to see the shops lit up. Every lamp post had a fir tree tied to it—not corpsy old trees but fresh cut firs. Victoria streets were dark; this made the shops look all the brighter. Windows were decorated with mock snow made of cotton wool and diamond dust. Drygoods shops did not have much that was Christmassy to display except red flannel and rabbit fur baby coats and muffs and tippets. Chemists had immense globes of red, green and blue medicine hanging from brass chains in their shop windows. I wished some of us could be sick enough for Dr. Helmcken to prescribe one of the splendid globes for us. The chemists also showed coloured soap and fancy perfume in bottles. Castor oil in hideous blue bottles peered from behind nice Christmas things and threw out hints about overeating and stomach-ache. A horrid woman once told my mother that she let her children eat everything they wanted on Christmas Day and finished them up with a big dose of castor oil. Mr. Hibben, the stationer, was nicer than that woman and the chemist. He hid all the school books behind story books left open at the best pictures. He had "Merry Christmas" in cotton wool on red cardboard in his window.

It was the food shops that Merry Christmassed the hardest. In Mr. Saunder's, the grocer's, window was a real Santa Claus grinding coffee. The wheel was bigger than he was. He had a long beard and moved his hands and his head. As the wheel went round the coffee beans went in, got ground, and came out, smell and all. In the window all round Santa were bonbons, cluster raisins, nuts and candied fruit, besides long walking-sticks made of peppermint candy. Next to this splendid window came Goodacre's horrible butcher shop—everything in it dead and naked. Dead geese and turkeys waggled, head down; dead beeves, calves and pigs straddled between immense meat hooks on the walls; naked sheep had bunches of coloured paper where their heads ought to have been and flowers and squiggles carved in the fat of their backs. Creatures that still had their heads on stared out of eyes like poached eggs when the white has run over the yolk. Baby pigs looked worst of all—pink and naked as bathing babies, their cheeks drawn back to make them smile at the red apples which had been forced into their toothless, sucking mouths. The shop floor was strewn deep in sawdust to catch blood drips. You heard no footsteps in the shop, only the sharpening of knives, sawing of bones, and bump, bump of the scale. Everybody was examining meat and saying, "Compliments of the Season" to everyone else, Father saying, "Fine display, Goodacre, very fine indeed!" We children rushed out and went back to Santa while Father chose his meat.

The shop of old George, the poulterer, was nearly as bad as Goodacre's, only the dead things did not look so dead, nor stare so hard, having shut the grey lids over their eyes to die. They were limp in necks and stiff in legs. As most of them had feathers on they looked like birds still, whereas the butcher's creatures had been rushed at once from life to meat.

The food shops ended the town, and after that came Johnson Street and Chinatown, which was full of black night. Here we turned back towards James' Bay, ready for bed.

There was a high mantelpiece in the breakfast room. And while we were hanging our stockings from it my sister read:

> "'Twas the night before Christmas and all through the house
> Not a creature was stirring, not even a mouse."

On the way to bed we could smell our Christmas tree waiting in the dining-room. The room was all dark but we knew that it stood on the floor and touched the ceiling and that it hung heavy with presents, ready for to-morrow. When the lights were lit there would be more of them than any of us children could count. We would all take hands and sing carols round the tree; Bong would come in and look with his mouth open. There was always things on it for him but he would not wait to get his presents. He would run back to his kitchen and we would take them to him there. It seemed as if Bong felt too Chinese to Christmas with us in our Canadian way.

Present-giving was only done to members in one's immediate family. Others you gave love and a card to, and kissed the people you did not usually kiss.

Pickwick on *Ice*

by
CHARLES DICKENS
(1812–1870)

*Pickwick's skating party forms a part of his Christmas Day fes-
tivities, and so falls roundly—not to put too nice a point on it—
within the limits of this collection. There are moments, perhaps,
when Mr. Pickwick himself is seen in not quite the kindliest of
lights—as when he takes exception to poor Winkle's dubious
skating abilities—but on the whole the party comes off with
about as much success as might be expected, and Sam Weller's
prowess as a master of fancy sliding is a priceless piece of
Dickensian illogic.*

163

"**N**ow," said Wardle, after a substantial lunch, with the agreeable items of strong-beer and cherry-brandy, had been done ample justice to, "what say you to an hour on the ice? We shall have plenty of time."

"Capital!" said Mr Benjamin Allen.

"Prime!" ejaculated Mr Bob Sawyer.

"You skate, of course, Winkle?" said Wardle.

"Ye-yes, oh yes," replied Mr Winkle. "I—I—am *rather* out of practice."

"Oh, *do* skate, Mr Winkle," said Arabella. "I like to see it so much."

"Oh, it is *so* graceful," said another young lady.

A third young lady said it was elegant, and a fourth expressed her opinion that it was "swan-like."

"I should be very happy, I'm sure," said Mr Winkle, reddening; "but I have no skates."

This objection was at once overruled. Trundle had a couple of pair, and the fat boy announced that there were half a dozen more downstairs; whereat Mr Winkle expressed exquisite delight, and looked exquisitely uncomfortable.

Old Wardle led the way to a pretty large sheet of ice; and the fat boy and Mr Weller having shovelled and swept away the snow which had fallen on it during the night, Mr Bob Sawyer adjusted his skates with a dexterity which to Mr Winkle was perfectly marvellous, and prescribed circles with his left leg, and cut figures of eight, and inscribed upon the ice, without once stopping for breath, a great many other pleasant and astonishing devices, to the excessive satisfaction of Mr Pickwick, Mr Tupman, and the ladies; which reached a pitch of positive enthusiasm when old Wardle and Benjamin Allen, assisted by the aforesaid Bob Sawyer, performed some mystic evolutions which they called a reel.

All this time Mr Winkle, with his face and hands blue with the cold, had been forcing a gimlet into the soles of his feet, and putting his skates on with the points behind, and getting the straps into a very complicated and entangled state, with the assistance of Mr Snodgrass, who knew rather less about skates than a Hindoo. At length, however, with the assistance of Mr Weller, the unfortunate skates were firmly screwed and buckled on, and Mr Winkle was raised to his feet.

"Now, then, sir," said Sam, in an encouraging tone; "off vith you, and show 'em how to do it."

"Stop, Sam, stop!" said Mr Winkle, trembling violently, and clutching hold of Sam's arms with the grasp of a drowning man. "How slippery it is, Sam!"

"Not an uncommon thing upon ice, sir," replied Mr Weller. "Hold up, sir!"

This last observation of Mr Weller's bore reference to a demonstration Mr Winkle made, at the instant, of a frantic desire to throw his feet in the air and dash the back of his head on the ice.

"These—these—are very awkward skates; ain't they, Sam?" inquired Mr Winkle, staggering.

"I'm afeerd there's a orkard gen'l'm'n in 'em, sir," replied Sam.

"Now, Winkle," cried Mr Pickwick, quite unconscious that there was anything the matter. "Come; the ladies are all anxiety."

"Yes, yes," replied Mr Winkle, with a ghastly smile; "I'm coming."

"Just a-goin' to begin," said Sam, endeavouring to disengage himself. "Now, sir, start off!"

"Stop an instant, Sam," gasped Mr Winkle, clinging most affectionately to Mr Weller. "I find I've got a couple of coats at home that I don't want, Sam. You may have them, Sam."

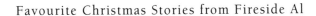

"Thank'ee, sir," replied Mr Weller.

"Never mind touching your hat, Sam," said Mr Winkle, hastily; "you needn't take your hand away to do that. I meant to have given you five shillings this morning for a Christmas box, Sam. I'll give it you this afternoon, Sam."

"You're wery good, sir," replied Mr Weller.

"Just hold me at first, Sam; will you?" said Mr Winkle. "There—that's right. I shall soon get in the way of it, Sam. Not too fast, Sam; not too fast."

Mr Winkle, stooping forward with his body half doubled up, was being assisted over the ice by Mr Weller, in a very singular and unswanlike manner, when Mr Pickwick most innocently shouted from the opposite bank:

"Sam!"

"Sir?" said Mr Weller.

"Here. I want you."

"Let go, sir," said Sam. "Don't you hear the governor a-callin'? Let go, sir."

With a violent effort, Mr Weller disengaged himself from the grasp of the agonized Pickwickian, and in so doing administered a considerable impetus to the unhappy Mr Winkle. With an accuracy which no degree of dexterity or practice could have ensured, that unfortunate gentleman bore swiftly down into the centre of the reel, at the very moment when Mr Bob Sawyer was performing a flourish of unparalleled beauty. Mr Winkle struck wildly against him, and with a loud crash they both fell heavily down. Mr Pickwick ran to the spot. Bob Sawyer had risen to his feet, but Mr Winkle was far too wise to do anything of the kind in skates. He was seated on the ice, making spasmodic efforts to smile; but anguish was depicted on every lineament of his countenance.

"Are you hurt?" inquired Mr Benjamin Allen, with great anxiety.

"Not much," said Mr Winkle, rubbing his back very hard.

"I wish you'd let me bleed you," said Mr Benjamin, with great eagerness.

"No, thank you," replied Mr Winkle, hurriedly.

"I really think you had better," said Allen.

"Thank you," replied Mr Winkle, "I'd rather not."

"What do *you* think, Mr Pickwick?" inquired Bob Sawyer.

Mr Pickwick was excited and indignant. He beckoned to Mr Weller and said, in a stern voice, "Take his skates off."

"No; but really I had scarcely begun," remonstrated Mr Winkle.

"Take his skates off," repeated Mr Pickwick, firmly.

The command was not to be resisted. Mr Winkle allowed Sam to obey in silence.

"Lift him up," said Mr Pickwick. Sam assisted him to rise.

Mr Pickwick retired a few paces apart from the bystanders, and beckoning his friend to approach, fixed a searching look upon him, and uttered, in a low but distinct and emphatic tone, these remarkable words:

"You're a humbug, sir."

"A what?" said Mr Winkle, starting.

"A humbug, sir. I will speak plainer, if you wish it. An impostor, sir."

With these words Mr Pickwick turned slowly on his heel, and rejoined his friends.

While Mr Pickwick was delivering himself of the sentiment just recorded, Mr Weller and the fat boy, having by their joint endeavours cut out a slide, were exercising themselves thereupon in a very masterly and brilliant manner. Sam Weller, in particular, was displaying that beautiful feat of fancy sliding which is currently denominated "knocking at the cobbler's door," and which is achieved by skimming over the ice on one foot, and occasionally giving a twopenny postman's knock upon it with the other. It was a good long slide, and there was something in the motion which Mr Pickwick, who was very cold with standing still, could not help envying.

"It looks nice, warm exercise that, doesn't it?" he inquired of Wardle, when that gentleman was thoroughly out of breath by reason of the indefatigable manner in which he had converted his legs into a pair of compasses, and drawn complicated problems on the ice.

"Ah, it does indeed," replied Wardle. "Do you slide?"

"I used to do so, on the gutters, when I was a boy," replied Mr Pickwick.

"Try it now," said Wardle.

"Oh, do, please, Mr Pickwick!" cried all the ladies.

"I should be very happy to afford you any amusement," replied Mr Pickwick, "but I haven't done such a thing these thirty years."

"Pooh! pooh! Nonsense!" said Wardle, dragging off his skates with the impetuosity which characterized all his proceedings. "Here; I'll keep you company. Come along!" And away went the good-tempered old fellow down the slide, with a rapidity which came very close upon Mr Weller, and beat the fat boy all to nothing.

Mr Pickwick paused, considered, pulled off his gloves and put them in his hat; took two or three short runs, balked himself as often, and at last took another run, and went slowly and gravely down the slide, with his feet about a yard and a quarter apart, amidst the gratified shouts of all the spectators.

"Keep the pot a-bilin', sir!" said Sam; and down went Wardle again, and then Mr Pickwick, and then Sam, and then Mr Winkle, and then Mr Bob Sawyer, and then the fat boy, and then Mr Snodgrass, following closely upon each other's heels, and running after each other with as much eagerness as if all their future prospects in life depended on their expedition.

It was the most intensely interesting thing to observe the manner in which Mr Pickwick performed his share in the ceremony; to watch the torture of anxiety with which he viewed the person behind, gaining upon him at the imminent hazard of tripping him up; to see him gradually expend the painful force which he had put on at first, and turn slowly round on the slide, with his face towards the point from which he had started; to contemplate the playful smile which mantled on his face when he had accomplished the distance, and the eagerness with which he turned round when he had done so and ran after his predecessor—his black gaiters tripping pleasantly through the snow, and his eyes beaming cheerfulness and gladness through his spectacles. And when he was knocked down (which happened upon the average every third round), it was the most invigorating sight that can possibly be imagined to behold him gather up his hat, gloves, and handkerchief, with a glowing countenance, and resume his station in the rank with an ardour and enthusiasm that nothing could abate.

The sport was at its height, the sliding was at the quickest, the laughter was at the loudest, when a sharp, smart crack was heard. There was a quick rush towards the bank, a wild scream from the ladies, and a shout from Mr Tupman. A large mass of ice disappeared; the water bubbled up over it; Mr Pickwick's hat, gloves, and handkerchiefs were floating on the surface; and this was all of Mr Pickwick that anybody could see.

Dismay and anguish were depicted on every countenance; the males turned pale, and the females fainted; Mr Snodgrass and Mr Winkle grasped each other by the hand, and gazed at the spot where their leader had gone down, with frenzied eagerness; while Mr Tupman, by way of rendering the promptest assistance, and at the same time conveying to any persons who might be within hearing the clearest possible notion of the catastrophe, ran off across the country at his utmost speed, screaming "Fire!" with all his might.

It was at this very moment, when old Wardle and Sam Weller were approaching the hole with cautious steps, and Mr Benjamin Allen was holding a hurried consultation with Mr Bob Sawyer on the advisability of bleeding the company generally, as an improving little bit of professional practice—it was at this very moment that a face, head, and shoulders emerged from beneath the water, and disclosed the features and spectacles of Mr Pickwick.

"Keep yourself up for an instant—for only one instant!" bawled Mr Snodgrass.

"Yes, do; let me implore you—for my sake!" roared Mr Winkle, deeply affected. The adjuration was rather unnecessary—the probability being that if Mr Pickwick had declined to keep himself up for anybody else's sake, it would have occurred to him that he might as well do so for his own.

"Do you feel the bottom there, old fellow?" said Wardle.

"Yes, certainly," replied Mr Pickwick, wringing the water from his head and face, and gasping for breath. "I fell upon my back. I couldn't get on my feet at first."

The clay upon so much of Mr Pickwick's coat as was yet visible bore testimony to the accuracy of this statement; and as the fears of the spectators were still further relieved by the fat boy's suddenly recollecting that the water was nowhere more than five feet deep, prodigies of valour were performed to get him out. After a vast quantity of splashing, and cracking, and struggling, Mr Pickwick was at length fairly extricated from his unpleasant position, and once more stood on dry land.

"Oh, he'll catch his death of cold," said Emily.

"Dear old thing!" said Arabella. "Let me wrap this shawl round you, Mr Pickwick."

"Ah, that's the best thing you can do," said Wardle; "and when you've got it on, run home as fast as your legs can carry you, and jump into bed directly."

A dozen shawls were offered on the instant. Three or four of the thickest having been selected, Mr Pickwick was wrapped up, and started off, under the guidance of Mr Weller—presenting the singular phenomenon of an elderly gentleman, dripping wet, and without a hat, with his arms bound down to his sides, skimming over the ground, without any clearly-defined purpose, at the rate of six good English miles an hour.

But Mr Pickwick cared not for appearances in such an extreme case, and urged on by Sam Weller, he kept at the very top of his speed until he reached the door of Manor Farm, where Mr Tupman had arrived some five minutes before, and had frightened the old lady into palpitations of the heart by impressing her with the unalterable conviction that the kitchen chimney was on fire—a calamity which always presented itself in glowing colours to the old lady's mind when anybody about her evinced the smallest agitation.

Mr Pickwick paused not an instant until he was snug in bed.

Bishop's Punch

An Oxford Recipe

Just the thing to warm up our frozen Pickwickians, a toddy that dates back to the earliest times. Older than the ages—older even than the venerable Pickwick. As a note of interest, Micawber's famous lemon-and-rum concoction in David Copperfield is, I think, a close variation of the Bishop's punch described below—rum having, for Micawber, the added and particularly endearing quality of relative cheapness, as opposed to the more costly port used here.

Bishop's Punch

Lemon
cloves
half a pint of water
cinnamon
mace
allspice
ginger
port wine
sugar

Take a lemon and make incisions in the rind. Stick cloves in these incisions and roast the lemon in front of a slow fire. Put into a saucepan half a pint of water with a little cinnamon and the same amount of cloves, mace, allspice and ginger. Boil it till it is reduced to a quarter of a pint. Empty a bottle of port wine into another saucepan and set fire to it while it is in the saucepan, to burn a little of the spirit out of it. Add the roasted lemon and the spiced water. Stir altogether and let it stand near the fire for ten minutes.

Rub some sugar on the rind of a lemon, and put it into a bowl with the juice of half a lemon. Pour the wine on it, grate in a little nutmeg, sweeten it to taste, and serve it with the lemon and spice floating in it.

A roasted Seville orange stuck with cloves can be used instead of a lemon.

The
Snow Image
A Childish Miracle

by
NATHANIEL HAWTHORNE
(1804–1864)

What was it that D.H. Lawrence said about Nathaniel Hawthorne? "Our golden-haired boy Nathaniel has seen some most darkening things"—something like that. In "The Snow Image," however, Hawthorne gives full rein to the power of childish innocence, and gives us a story well-suited to the Christmas hearth.

O ne afternoon of a cold winter's day, when the sun shone forth with chilly brightness, after a long storm, two children asked leave of their mother to run out and play in the new-fallen snow. The elder child was a little girl, whom, because she was of a tender and modest disposition, and was thought to be very beautiful, her parents, and other people who were familiar with her, used to call Violet. But her brother was known by the style and title of Peony, on account of the ruddiness of his broad and round little phiz, which made everybody think of sunshine and great scarlet flowers. The father of these two children, a certain Mr. Lindsey, it is important to say, was an excellent but exceedingly matter-of-fact sort of man, a dealer in hardware, and was sturdily accustomed to take what is called the common-sense view of all matters that came under his consideration. With a heart about as tender as other people's, he had a head as hard and impenetrable, and therefore, perhaps, as empty, as one of the iron pots which it was a part of his business to sell. The mother's character, on the other hand, had a strain of poetry in it, a trait of unworldly beauty—a delicate and dewy flower, as it were, that had survived out of her imaginative youth, and still kept itself alive amid the dusty realities of matrimony and motherhood.

So, Violet and Peony, as I began with saying, besought their mother to let them run out and play in the new snow; for, though it had looked so dreary and dismal, drifting downward out of the gray sky, it had a very cheerful aspect, now that the sun was shining on it. The children dwelt in a city, and had no wider play place than a little garden before the house, divided by a white fence from the street, and with a pear tree and two or three plum trees overshadowing it, and some rosebushes just in front of the parlor windows. The trees and shrubs, however, were now leafless, and their twigs were enveloped in the slight snow, which thus made a kind of wintry foliage, with here and there a pendent icicle for the fruit.

"Yes, Violet—yes, my little Peony," said their kind mother, "you may go out and play in the new snow."

Accordingly, the good lady bundled up her darlings in woolen jackets and wadded sacks, and put comforters around their necks, and a pair of striped gaiters on each little pair of legs, and worsted mittens on their hands, and gave them a kiss apiece, by way of a spell to keep away Jack Frost. Forth sallied the two children with a hop-skip-and-jump that carried them at once into the very heart of a huge snowdrift, whence Violet emerged like a snow bunting, while little Peony floundered out with his round face in full bloom. Then what a merry time had they! To look at them, frolicking in the wintry garden, you would have thought that the dark and pitiless storm had been sent for no other purpose but to provide a new plaything for Violet and Peony; and that they themselves had been created, as the snowbirds were, to take delight only in the tempest and in the white mantle which it spread over the earth.

At last, when they had frosted one another all over with handfuls of snow, Violet, after laughing heartily at little Peony's figure, was struck with a new idea.

"You look exactly like a snow image, Peony," said she, "if your cheeks were not so red. And that puts me in mind! Let us make an image out of snow—an image of a little girl—and it shall be our sister, and shall run about and play with us all winter long. Won't it be nice?"

"Oh, yes!" cried Peony, as plainly as he could speak, for he was but a little boy. "That will be nice! And Mama shall see it!"

"Yes," answered Violet; "Mama shall see the new little girl. But she must not make her come into the warm parlor; for, you know, our little snow sister will not love the warmth."

And forthwith the children began this great business of making a snow image that should run about; while their mother, who was sitting at the window and overheard some of their talk, could not help smiling at the gravity with which they set about it. They really seemed to imagine that there would be no difficulty whatever in creating a live little girl out of the snow. And, to say the truth, if miracles are ever to be wrought, it will be by putting our hands to the work in precisely such a simple and undoubting frame of mind as that in which Violet and Peony now undertook to perform one, without so much as knowing that it was a miracle. So thought the mother; and thought, likewise, that the new snow, just fallen from heaven, would be excellent material to make new beings of, if it were not so very cold. She gazed at the children a moment longer, delighting to watch their little figures—the girl, tall for her age, graceful and agile, and so delicately colored that she looked like a cheerful thought more than a physical reality; while Peony expanded in breadth rather than height, and rolled along on his short and sturdy legs as substantial as an elephant, though not quite so big. Then the mother resumed her work. What it was I forget; but she was either trimming a silken bonnet for Violet or darning a pair of stockings for little Peony's short legs. Again, however, and again, and yet other agains, she could not help turning her head to the window to see how the children got on with their snow image.

Indeed, it was an exceedingly pleasant sight, those bright little souls at their task! Moreover, it was really wonderful to observe how knowingly and skilfully they managed the matter. Violet assumed the chief direction and told Peony what to do, while, with her own delicate fingers, she shaped out all the nicer parts of the snow figure. It seemed, in fact, not so much to be made by the children, as to grow up under their hands, while they were playing and prattling about it. Their mother was quite surprised at this; and the longer she looked, the more and more surprised she grew.

"What remarkable children mine are!" thought she, smiling with a mother's pride; and, smiling at herself, too, for being so proud of them. "What other children could have made anything so like a little girl's figure out of snow at the first trial? Well; but now I must finish Peony's new frock, for his grandfather is coming tomorrow, and I want the little fellow to look handsome."

So she took up the frock, and was soon as busily at work again with her needle as the two children with their snow image. But still, as the needle traveled hither and thither through the seams of the dress, the mother made her toil light and happy by listening to the airy voices of Violet and Peony. They kept talking to one another all the time, their tongues being quite as active as their feet and hands. Except at intervals, she could not distinctly hear what was said, but had merely a sweet impression that they were in a most loving mood and were enjoying themselves highly, and that the business of making the snow image went prosperously on. Now and then, however, when Violet and Peony happened to raise their voices, the words were as audible as if they had been spoken in the very parlor where the mother sat. Oh, how delightfully those words echoed in her heart, even though they meant nothing so very wise or wonderful, after all!

But you must know a mother listens with her heart much more than with her ears; and thus she is often delighted with the trills of celestial music, when other people can hear nothing of the kind.

"Peony, Peony!" cried Violet to her brother, who had gone to another part of the garden, "bring me some of that fresh snow, Peony, from the very farthest corner, where we have not been trampling. I want it to shape our little snow sister's bosom with. You know that part must be quite pure, just as it came out of the sky!"

"Here it is, Violet!" answered Peony, in his bluff tone—but a very sweet tone, too—as he came floundering through the half-trodden drifts. "Here is the snow for her little bosom. Oh, Violet, how beau-ti-ful she begins to look!"

"Yes," said Violet, thoughtfully and quietly; "our snow sister does look very lovely. I did not quite know, Peony, that we could make such a sweet little girl as this."

The mother, as she listened, thought how fit and delightful an incident it would be if fairies, or still better, if angel children were to come from paradise, and play invisibly with her own darlings, and help them to make their snow image, giving it the features of celestial babyhood! Violet and Peony would not be aware of their immortal playmates—only they would see that the image grew very beautiful while they worked at it and would think that they themselves had done it all.

"My little girl and boy deserve such playmates, if mortal children ever did!" said the mother to herself, and then she smiled again at her own motherly pride.

Nevertheless, the idea seized upon her imagination and, ever and anon, she took a glimpse out of the window, half dreaming that she might see the golden-haired children of paradise sporting with her own golden-haired Violet and bright-cheeked Peony.

Now, for a few moments, there was a busy and earnest but indistinct hum of the two children's voices, as Violet and Peony wrought together with one happy consent. Violet still seemed to be the guiding spirit, while Peony acted rather as a laborer and brought her the snow from far and near. And yet the little urchin evidently had a proper understanding of the matter, too!

"Peony, Peony!" cried Violet; for her brother was again at the other side of the garden. "Bring me those light wreaths of snow that have rested on the lower branches of the pear tree. You can clamber on the snowdrift, Peony, and reach them easily. I must have them to make some ringlets for our snow sister's head!"

"Here they are, Violet!" answered the little boy. "Take care you do not break them. Well done! Well done! How pretty!"

"Does she not look sweetly?" said Violet, with a very satisfied tone; "and now we must have some little shining bits of ice, to make the brightness of her eyes. She is not finished yet. Mama will see how very beautiful she is; but Papa will say, 'Tush! nonsense! Come in out of the cold!'"

"Let us call Mama to look out," said Peony, and then he shouted lustily, "Mama! Mama!! Mama!!! Look out and see what a nice 'ittle girl we are making!"

The mother put down her work for an instant and looked out of the window. But it so happened that the sun—for this was one of the shortest days of the whole year—had sunk so nearly to the edge of the world that his setting shine came obliquely into the lady's eyes. So she was dazzled, you must understand,

and could not very distinctly observe what was in the garden. Still, however, through all that bright, blinding dazzle of the sun and the new snow, she beheld a small white figure in the garden that seemed to have a wonderful deal of human likeness about it. And she saw Violet and Peony—indeed, she looked more at them than at the image—she saw the two children still at work; Peony bringing fresh snow, and Violet applying it to the figure as scientifically as a sculptor adds clay to his model. Indistinctly as she discerned the snow child, the mother thought to herself that never before was there a snow figure so cunningly made, nor ever such a dear little girl and boy to make it.

"They do everything better than other children," said she, very complacently. "No wonder they make better snow images!"

She sat down again to her work, and made as much haste with it as possible; because twilight would soon come, and Peony's frock was not yet finished, and Grandfather was expected, by railroad, pretty early in the morning. Faster and faster, therefore, went her flying fingers. The children, likewise, kept busily at work in the garden, and still the mother listened, whenever she could catch a word. She was amused to observe how their little imaginations had got mixed up with what they were doing, and carried away by it. They seemed positively to think that the snow child would run about and play with them.

"What a nice playmate she will be for us, all winter long!" said Violet. "I hope Papa will not be afraid of her giving us a cold! Sha'n't you love her dearly, Peony?"

"Oh, yes!" cried Peony. "And I will hug her, and she shall sit down close by me and drink some of my warm milk!"

"Oh, no, Peony!" answered Violet with grave wisdom. "That will not do at all. Warm milk will not be wholesome for our little snow sister. Little snow people like her eat nothing but icicles. No, no, Peony; we must not give her anything warm to drink!"

There was a minute or two of silence; for Peony, whose short legs were never weary, had gone on a pilgrimage again to the other side of the garden. All of a sudden, Violet cried out, loudly and joyfully—

"Look here, Peony! Come quickly! A light has been shining on her cheek out of that rose-colored cloud! And the color does not go away! Is not that beautiful!"

"Yes; it is beau-ti-ful," answered Peony, pronouncing the three syllables with deliberate accuracy. "Oh, Violet, only look at her hair! It is all like gold!"

"Oh, certainly," said Violet, with tranquillity, as if it were very much a matter of course. "That color, you know, comes from the golden clouds that we see up there in the sky. She is almost finished now. But her lips must be made very red—redder than her cheeks. Perhaps, Peony, it will make them red if we both kiss them!"

Accordingly, the mother heard two smart little smacks, as if both her children were kissing the snow image on its frozen mouth. But, as this did not seem to make the lips quite red enough, Violet next proposed that the snow child should be invited to kiss Peony's scarlet cheek.

"Come, 'ittle snow sister, kiss me!" cried Peony.

"There! She has kissed you," added Violet, "and now her lips are very red. And she blushed a little, too!"

"Oh, what a cold kiss!" cried Peony.

Just then there came a breeze of the pure west wind, sweeping through the garden and rattling the parlor windows. It sounded so wintry cold that the mother was about to tap on the windowpane with her thimbled finger, to summon the two children in, when they both cried out to her with one voice. The tone was not a tone of surprise, although they were evidently a good deal excited; it appeared rather as if they were very much rejoiced at some event that had now happened, but which they had been looking for, and had reckoned upon all along.

"Mama! Mama! We have finished our little snow sister, and she is running about the garden with us!"

"What imaginative little beings my children are!" thought the mother, putting the last few stitches into Peony's frock. "And it is strange, too, that they make me almost as much a child as they themselves are! I can hardly help believing, now, that the snow image has really come to life!"

"Dear Mama!" cried Violet, "pray look out and see what a sweet playmate we have!"

The mother, being thus entreated, could no longer delay to look forth from the window. The sun was now gone out of the sky, leaving, however, a rich inheritance of his brightness among those purple and golden clouds which make the sunsets of winter so magnificent. But there was not the slightest gleam or dazzle, either on the window or on the snow; so that the good lady could look all over the garden and see everything and everybody in it. And what do you think she saw there? Violet and Peony, of course, her own two darling children. Ah, but whom or what did she see besides? Why, if you will believe me, there was a small figure of a girl, dressed all in white, with rose-tinged cheeks and ringlets of golden hue, playing about the garden with the two children! A stranger though she was, the child seemed to be on as familiar terms with Violet and Peony, and they with her, as if all the three had been playmates during the whole of their little lives. The mother thought to herself that it must certainly be the daughter of one of the neighbors, and that, seeing Violet and Peony in the garden, the child had run across the street to play with them. So this kind lady went to the door, intending to invite the little runaway into her comfortable parlor; for, now that the sunshine was withdrawn, the atmosphere, out of doors, was already growing very cold.

But, after opening the house door, she stood an instant on the threshold, hesitating whether she ought to ask the child to come in, or whether she should even speak to her. Indeed, she almost doubted whether it were a real child after all, or only a light wreath of the new-fallen snow, blown hither and thither about the garden by the intensely cold west wind. There was certainly something very singular in the aspect of the little stranger. Among all the children of the neighborhood, the lady could remember no such face, with its pure white, and delicate rose color, and the golden ringlets tossing about the forehead and cheeks. And as for her dress, which was entirely white, and fluttering in the breeze, it was such as no reasonable woman would put upon a little girl, when sending her out to play, in the depth of winter. It made this kind and careful mother shiver only to look at those small feet, with nothing in the world on them except a very thin pair of white slippers. Nevertheless, airily as she was clad, the child seemed to feel not the slightest inconvenience from the cold, but danced so lightly over the snow that the tips of her toes left hardly a print in its surface; while Violet could but just keep pace with her, and Peony's short legs compelled him to lag behind.

Once, in the course of their play, the strange child placed herself between Violet and Peony, and taking a hand of each, skipped merrily forward, and they along with her. Almost immediately, however, Peony pulled away his little fist, and began to rub it as if the fingers were tingling with cold; while Violet also released herself, though with less abruptness, gravely remarking that it was better not to take hold of hands. The white-robed damsel said not a word, but danced about just as merrily as before. If Violet and Peony did not choose to play with her, she could make just as good a playmate of the brisk and cold west wind, which kept blowing her all about the garden, and took such liberties with her that they seemed to have been friends for a long time. All this while, the mother stood on the threshold, wondering how a little girl could look so much like a flying snowdrift, or how a snowdrift could look so very like a little girl.

She called Violet and whispered to her.

"Violet, my darling, what is this child's name?" asked she. "Does she live near us?"

"Why, dearest Mama," answered Violet, laughing to think that her mother did not comprehend so very plain an affair, "this is our little snow sister whom we have just been making!"

"Yes, dear Mama," cried Peony, running to his mother and looking up simply into her face. "This is our snow image! Is it not a nice 'ittle child?"

At this instant a flock of snowbirds came flitting through the air. As was very natural, they avoided Violet and Peony. But—and this looked strange—they flew at once to the white-robed child, fluttered eagerly about her head, alighted on her shoulders, and seemed to claim her as an old acquaintance. She, on her part, was evidently as glad to see these little birds, old Winter's grandchildren, as they were to see her, and welcomed them by holding out both her hands. Hereupon, they each and all tried to alight on her two palms and ten small fingers and thumbs, crowding one another off, with an immense fluttering of their tiny wings. One dear little bird nestled tenderly in her bosom; another put its bill to her lips. They were as joyous, all the while, and seemed as much in their element, as you may have seen them when sporting with a snow-storm.

Violet and Peony stood laughing at this pretty sight, for they enjoyed the merry time which their new playmate was having with these small-winged visitants almost as much as if they themselves took part in it.

"Violet," said her mother, greatly perplexed, "tell me the truth, without any jest. Who is this little girl?"

"My darling Mama," answered Violet, looking seriously into her mother's face, and apparently surprised that she should need any further explanation, "I have told you truly who she is. It is our little snow image, which Peony and I have been making. Peony will tell you so, as well as I."

"Yes, Mama," asseverated Peony, with much gravity in his crimson little phiz; "this is 'ittle snow child. Is not she a nice one? But, Mama, her hand is, oh, so very cold!"

While Mama still hesitated what to think and what to do, the street gate was thrown open, and the father of Violet and Peony appeared, wrapped in a pilot-cloth sack, with a fur cap drawn down over his ears, and the thickest of gloves upon his hands. Mr. Lindsey was a middle-aged man with a weary and yet a happy look in his wind-flushed and frost-pinched face, as if he had been busy all the day long and was glad to get back to his quiet home. His eyes brightened at the sight of his wife and children, although he could not help uttering a word or two of surprise at finding the whole family in the open air on so bleak a day, and after sunset, too. He soon perceived the little white stranger sporting to and fro in the garden, like a dancing snow wreath, and the flock of snowbirds fluttering about her head.

"Pray, what little girl may that be?" inquired this very sensible man. "Surely her mother must be crazy to let her go out in such bitter weather as it has been today with only that flimsy white gown and those thin slippers!"

"My dear husband," said his wife, "I know no more about the little thing than you do. Some neighbor's child, I suppose. Our Violet and Peony," she added, laughing at herself for repeating so absurd a story, "insist that she is nothing but a snow image, which they have been busy about in the garden almost all the afternoon."

As she said this, the mother glanced her eyes toward the spot where the children's snow image had been made. What was her surprise, on perceiving that there was not the slightest trace of so much labor!—no image at all!—no piled-up heap of snow!—nothing whatever, save the prints of little footsteps around a vacant space!

"This is very strange!" said she.

"What is strange, dear Mother?" asked Violet. "Dear Father, do not you see how it is? This is our snow image, which Peony and I have made because we wanted another playmate. Did not we, Peony?"

"Yes, Papa," said crimson Peony. "This be our 'ittle snow sister. Is she not beau-ti-ful? But she gave me such a cold kiss!"

"Poh, nonsense, children!" cried their good, honest father, who, as we have already intimated, had an exceedingly common-sensible way of looking at matters. "Do not tell me of making live figures out of snow. Come, wife; this little stranger must not stay out in the bleak air a moment longer. We will bring her into the parlor; and you shall give her a supper of warm bread and milk, and make her as comfortable as you can. Meanwhile, I will inquire among the neighbors; or, if necessary, send the city crier about the streets to give notice of a lost child."

So saying, this honest and very kindhearted man was going toward the little white damsel with the best intentions in the world. But Violet and Peony, each seizing their father by the hand, earnestly besought him not to make her come in.

"Dear Father," cried Violet, putting herself before him, "it is true what I have been telling you! This is our little snowgirl, and she cannot live any longer than while she breathes the cold west wind. Do not make her come into the hot room!"

"Yes, Father," shouted Peony, stamping his little foot, so mightily was he in earnest, "this be nothing but our 'ittle snow child! She will not love the hot fire!"

"Nonsense, children, nonsense, nonsense!" cried the father, half vexed, half laughing at what he considered their foolish obstinacy. "Run into the house, this moment! It is too late to play any longer, now. I must take care of this little girl immediately, or she will catch her death-a-cold!"

"Husband! Dear husband!" said his wife, in a low voice—for

she had been looking narrowly at the snow child, and was more perplexed than ever—"there is something very singular in all this. You will think me foolish, but—but—may it not be that some invisible angel has been attracted by the simplicity and good faith with which our children set about their undertaking? May he not have spent an hour of his immortality in playing with those dear little souls? ...and so the result is what we call a miracle. No, no! Do not laugh at me; I see what a foolish thought it is!"

"My dear wife," replied the husband, laughing heartily, "you are as much a child as Violet and Peony."

And in one sense so she was, for all through life she had kept her heart full of childlike simplicity and faith, which was as pure and clear as crystal, and, looking at all matters through this transparent medium, she sometimes saw truths so profound that other people laughed at them as nonsense and absurdity.

But now kind Mr. Lindsey had entered the garden, breaking away from his two children, who still sent their shrill voices after him, beseeching him to let the snowchild stay and enjoy herself in the cold west wind.

As he approached, the snowbirds took to flight. The little white damsel, also, fled backward, shaking her head, as if to say, "Pray, do not touch me!" and roguishly, as it appeared, leading him through the deepest of the snow. Once, the good man stumbled and floundered down upon his face, so that, gathering himself up again, with the snow sticking to his rough pilot-cloth sack, he looked as white and wintry as a snow image of the largest size. Some of the neighbors, meanwhile, seeing him from their windows, wondered what could possess poor Mr. Lindsey to be running about his garden in pursuit of a snowdrift which the west wind was driving hither and thither! At length, after a vast deal of trouble, he chased the little stranger into a corner, where she could not possibly escape him. His wife had been looking on, and, it being nearly twilight, was wonderstruck to observe how the snow child gleamed and sparkled, and how she seemed to shed a glow all around about her; and when driven into the corner, she positively glistened like a star! It was a frosty kind of brightness, too, like that of an icicle in the moon-light. The wife thought it strange that good Mr. Lindsey should see nothing remarkable in the snow child's appearance.

"Come, you odd little thing!" cried the honest man, seizing her by the hand, "I have caught you at last, and will make you comfortable in spite of yourself. We will put a nice warm pair of worsted stockings on your frozen little feet, and you shall have a good thick shawl to wrap yourself in. Your poor white nose, I am afraid, is actually frostbitten. But we will make it all right. Come along in."

And so, with a most benevolent smile on his sagacious visage, all purple as it was with the cold, this very well-meaning gentleman took the snow child by the hand and led her toward the house. She followed him, droopingly and reluctant; for all the glow and sparkle were gone out of her figure; and whereas just before she had resembled a bright, frosty, star-gemmed evening, with a crimson gleam of the cold horizon, she now looked as dull and languid as a thaw. As kind Mr. Lindsey led her up the steps of the door, Violet and Peony looked into his face—their eyes full of tears which froze before they could run down their cheeks—and again entreated him not to bring their snow image into the house.

"Not bring her in!" exclaimed the kindhearted man. "Why, you are crazy, my little Violet!—quite crazy, my small Peony! She is so cold, already, that her hand has almost frozen mine, in spite of my thick gloves. Would you have her freeze to death?"

His wife, as he came up the steps, had been taking another long, earnest, almost awestricken gaze at the little white stranger. She hardly knew whether it was a dream or no, but she could not help fancying that she saw the delicate print of Violet's fingers on the child's neck. It looked just as if, while Violet was shaping out the image, she had given it a gentle pat with her hand, and had neglected to smooth the impression quite away.

"After all, husband," said the mother, recurring to her idea that the angels would be as much delighted to play with Violet and Peony as she herself was, "after all, she does look strangely like a snow image! I do believe she is made of snow!"

A puff of the west wind blew against the snow child, and again she sparkled like a star.

"Snow!" repeated good Mr. Lindsey, drawing the reluctant guest over his hospitable threshold. "No wonder she looks like snow. She is half frozen, poor little thing! But a good fire will put everything to rights!"

Without further talk, and always with the same best intentions, this highly benevolent and common-sensible individual led the little white damsel—drooping, drooping, drooping, more and more—out of the frosty air and into his comfortable parlor. A Heidenberg stove, filled to the brim with intensely burning anthracite, was sending a bright gleam through the isinglass of its iron door, and causing the vase of water on its top to fume and bubble with excitement. A warm, sultry smell was diffused throughout the room. A thermometer on the wall farthest from the stove stood at eighty degrees. The parlor was hung with red curtains, and covered with a red carpet, and looked just as warm as it felt. The difference betwixt the atmosphere here and the cold, wintry twilight out of doors was like stepping at once from Nova Zembla to the hottest part of India, or from the North Pole into an oven. Oh, this was a fine place for the little white stranger!

The common-sensible man placed the snow child on the hearth rug, right in front of the hissing and fuming stove.

"Now she will be comfortable!" cried Mr. Lindsey, rubbing his hands and looking about him with the pleasantest smile you ever saw. "Make yourself at home, my child."

Sad, sad and drooping, looked the little white maiden as she stood on the hearth rug, with the hot blast of the stove striking through her like a pestilence. Once, she threw a glance wistfully toward the windows and caught a glimpse, through its red curtains, of the snow-covered roofs, and the stars glimmering frostily, and all the delicious intensity of the cold night. The bleak wind rattled the windowpanes, as if it were summoning her to come forth. But there stood the snow child, drooping, before the hot stove!

But the common-sensible man saw nothing amiss.

"Come, wife," said he, "let her have a pair of thick stockings and a woolen shawl or blanket directly; and tell Dora to give her some warm supper as soon as the milk boils. You, Violet and Peony, amuse your little friend. She is out of spirits, you see, at finding herself in a strange place. For my part, I will go around among the neighbors and find out where she belongs."

The mother, meanwhile, had gone in search of the shawl and stockings; for her own view of the matter, however subtle and delicate, had given way, as it always did, to the stubborn materialism of her husband. Without heeding the remonstrances of his two children, who still kept murmuring that their little snow sister did not love the warmth, good Mr. Lindsey took his departure, shutting the parlor door carefully behind him. Turning up the collar of his sack over his ears, he emerged from the house, and had barely reached the street gate, when he was recalled by the screams of Violet and Peony and the rapping of a thimbled finger against the parlor window.

"Husband! Husband!" cried his wife showing her horror-stricken face through the windowpanes. "There is no need of going for the child's parents!"

"We told you so, Father!" screamed Violet and Peony as he re-entered the parlor. "You would bring her in; and now our poor—dear—beau-ti-ful little snow sister is thawed!"

And their own sweet little faces were already dissolved in tears; so that their father, seeing what strange things occasionally happen in this everyday world, felt not a little anxious lest his children might be going to thaw, too! In the utmost perplexity, he demanded an explanation of his wife. She could only reply that, being summoned to the parlor by the cries of Violet and Peony, she found no trace of the little white maiden, unless it were the remains of a heap of snow, which, while she was gazing at it, melted quite away upon the hearth rug.

"And there you see all that is left of it!" added she, pointing to a pool of water in front of the stove.

"Yes, Father," said Violet looking reproachfully at him through her tears, "there is all that is left of our dear little snow sister!"

"Naughty Father!" cried Peony, stamping his foot, and—I shudder to say—shaking his little fist at the common-sensible man. "We told you how it would be! What for did you bring her in?"

And the Heidenberg stove, through the isinglass of its door, seemed to glare at good Mr. Lindsey, like a red-eyed demon, triumphing in the mischief which it had done!

This, you will observe, was one of those rare cases, which yet will occasionally happen, where common sense finds itself at fault. The remarkable story of the snow image, though to that sagacious class of people to whom good Mr. Lindsey belongs it may seem but a childish affair, is, nevertheless, capable of being moralized in various methods, greatly for their edification. One of its lessons, for instance, might be, that it behooves men, and especially men of benevolence, to consider well what they are about, and, before acting on their philanthropic purposes, to be quite sure that they comprehend the nature and all the relations of the business at hand. What has been established as an element of good to one being may prove absolute mischief to another; even as the warmth of the parlor was proper enough for children of flesh and blood, like Violet and Peony—though by no means very wholesome, even for them—but involved nothing short of annihilation to the unfortunate snow image.

But, after all, there is no teaching anything to wise men of good Mr. Lindsey's stamp. They know everything—oh, to be sure!—everything that has been, and everything that is, and everything that, by any future possibility, can be. And, should some phenomenon of nature or province transcend their system, they will not recognize it, even if it come to pass under their very noses.

"Wife," said Mr. Lindsey after a fit of silence, "see what a quantity of snow the children have brought in on their feet! It has made quite a puddle here before the stove. Pray tell Dora to bring some towels and sop it up!"

Gritibaenz

by

CAROL-ANNE MCCARTHY

A dough image (I can't believe I said that). This recipe for Gritibaenz (Swiss Doughmen or—better—Swiss Doughpeople) was first printed in the Canadian Children's Annual, *a venerable institution now sadly no longer in existence. By the way, these really are as tasty as they sound.*

Gritibaenz

It is a centuries-old tradition in Switzerland for Sinterklass (Santa Claus), dressed in a massive black coat with a hood and enormous black boots, to deliver Gritibaenz to the children on the eve of Saint Nicholas Day, December 6th. These glazed doughmen can sometimes measure up to two feet in length. They are available only on this festive occasion.

Katherine and Urs, friends from Switzerland, have particularly fond memories of their family, relatives, and friends going for a picnic in the forest on Saint Nicholas Day. They clipped candles to a fir tree and lit them while everyone sang carols. The biggest treat of all was when Sinterklass suddenly appeared out of nowhere with chocolates, apples, oranges, nuts, and the tasty doughmen. What a spectacular experience!

These doughmen are fun to make. We certainly look forward to these tantalizing treats served with hot chocolate every Christmas.

Ingredients:

1-3/4 cups milk scalded
2 envelopes of yeast
1/4 cup lukewarm water
1/2 cup sugar
1-1/4 teaspoons salt
1/2 cup butter or more if desired
5-1/2—6 cups flour

Instructions:

Dissolve yeast in lukewarm water with 1 teaspoon sugar; let stand 10 minutes. Put hot scalded milk, salt, butter and remaining sugar in a large warm bowl. When milk has cooled to lukewarm add yeast. Add enough flour gradually to make a soft dough. Turn dough out on a lightly

floured board and knead for 10 minutes, adding enough flour to prevent sticking. Place dough in a buttered bowl. Let rise until doubled; about 1 hour.

Punch the dough down. Take a handful of dough and shape into a fat sausage. Cut as shown in diagram. Separate arms and legs. If you pinch the head, the arms will open out. Use chocolate chips for eyes, nose, and buttons. Make sure you insert the chips well into the dough. Place on buttered cookie sheet. Place in a 200°F preheated oven for 10 minutes. Raise the temperature to 375° and glaze the doughmen with 1 egg yolk beaten with 1 teaspoon of water. Bake for another 15 minutes.

A
Child's Christmas
in Wales

by
DYLAN THOMAS
(1914–1953)

To think of poor Dylan Thomas reeling his way around the streets of New York City, and then to sit down and read his childhood reflections: to see the village of his youth through the older poet's eyes. "A Child's Christmas in Wales" is one of the finest series of Christmas recollections for reading around the fireside. At times you can sense the more vigorous hand of the older poet at work, but what remains foremost is the little boy with his "bags of moist and many-coloured jelly babies" walking down old Mumbles Road, or looking out his bedroom window "into the moonlight and the unending smoke-coloured snow."

195

ne Christmas was so much like another,
in those years around the sea-town corner now
and out of all sound except the distant speaking
of the voices I sometimes hear a moment before sleep,
that I can never remember whether it snowed
for six days and six nights when I was twelve
or whether it snowed for twelve days and
twelve nights when I was six.

All the Christmases roll down toward the
two-tongued sea, like a cold and headlong moon
bundling down the sky that was our street;
and they stop at the rim of the ice-edged,
fish-freezing waves, and I plunge my hands in the
snow and bring out whatever I find. In goes
my hand into that wool-white bell-tongued ball of
holidays resting at the rim of the carol-singing
sea, and out comes Mrs Prothero and the firemen.

It was on the afternoon of the day
of Christmas Eve, and I was in Mrs Prothero's
garden, waiting for cats, with her son Jim.
It was snowing. It was always snowing at Christmas.
December, in my memory, is white as Lapland,
though there were no reindeers.

But there were cats. Patient, cold and callous,
our hands wrapped in socks, we waited
to snowball the cats. Sleek and long as jaguars
and horrible-whiskered, spitting and snarling,
they would slink and sidle over the white
back-garden walls, and the lynx-eyed hunters,
Jim and I, fur-capped and moccasined trappers
from Hudson Bay, off Mumbles Road, would hurl
our deadly snowballs at the green of their eyes.

The wise cats never appeared. We were so still,
Eskimo-footed arctic marksmen in the muffling
silence of the eternal snows—eternal,
ever since Wednesday—that we never heard
Mrs Prothero's first cry from her igloo at the
bottom of her garden. Or, if we heard it at all,
it was, to us, like the far-off challenge of our enemy
and prey, the neighbour's polar cat. But soon the
voice grew louder. "Fire!" cried Mrs Prothero,
and she beat the dinner-gong.

And we ran down the garden, with the snowballs
in our arms, toward the house; and smoke,
indeed, was pouring out of the dining-room,
and the gong was bombilating, and Mrs Prothero
was announcing ruin like a town crier in Pompeii.
This was better than all the cats in Wales
standing on the wall in a row. We bounded into
the house, laden with snowballs, and stopped at
the open door of the smoke-filled room.

Something was burning all right;
perhaps it was Mr Prothero, who always slept
there after midday dinner with a newspaper
over his face. But he was standing in the middle
of the room, saying, "A fine Christmas!"
and smacking at the smoke with a slipper.
"Call the fire brigade," cried Mrs Prothero
as she beat the gong.

"They won't be there," said Mr Prothero,
"it's Christmas."

There was no fire to be seen, only clouds of smoke
and Mr Prothero standing in the middle of them,
waving his slipper as though he were conducting.

"Do something," he said.
And we threw all our snowballs into the smoke—
I think we missed Mr Prothero—and ran out
of the house to the telephone box.

"Let's call the police as well," Jim said.

"And the ambulance."

"And Ernie Jenkins, he likes fires."

But we only called the fire brigade, and soon
the fire engine came and three tall men in helmets
brought a hose into the house and Mr Prothero
got out just in time before they turned it on.
Nobody could have had a noisier Christmas Eve.
And when the firemen turned off the hose and
were standing in the wet, smoky room, Jim's aunt,
Miss Prothero, came downstairs and peered in
at them. Jim and I waited, very quietly, to hear what
she would say to them. She said the right thing,
always. She looked at the three tall firemen in their
shining helmets, standing among the smoke and
cinders and dissolving snowballs, and she said:
"Would you like anything to read?"

Years and years and years ago, when I was a boy,
when there were wolves in Wales, and birds
the colour of red-flannel petticoats whisked past
the harp-shaped hills, when we sang and wallowed
all night and day in caves that smelt like Sunday
afternoons in damp front farmhouse parlours,

and we chased, with the jawbones of deacons,
the English and the bears, before the motor-car,
before the wheel, before the duchess-faced horse,
when we rode the daft and happy hills bareback,
it snowed and it snowed. But here a small boy says:
"It snowed last year, too. I made a snowman and
my brother knocked it down and I knocked my
brother down and then we had tea."

"But that was not the same snow," I say.
"Our snow was not only shaken from whitewash
buckets down the sky, it came shawling out of the ground
and swam and drifted out of the arms and hands and
bodies of the trees; snow grew overnight on the
roofs of the houses like a pure and grandfather
moss, minutely white-ivied the walls and settled on
the postman, opening the gate, like a dumb, numb
thunderstorm of white, torn Christmas cards."

"Were there postmen then, too?"
"With sprinkling eyes and wind-cherried noses,
on spread, frozen feet they crunched up to the
doors and mittened on them manfully. But all that
the children could hear was a ringing of bells."

"You mean that the postman went rat-a-tat-tat
and the doors rang?"

"I mean that the bells that the children could
hear were inside them."

"I only hear thunder sometimes, never bells."

"There were church bells, too."

"Inside them?"

"No, no, no, in the bat-black, snow-white belfries,
tugged by bishops and storks. And they rang

their tidings over the bandaged town, over the
frozen foam of the powder and ice-cream hills,
over the crackling sea. It seemed that all the
churches boomed for joy under my window; and
the weathercocks crew for Christmas, on our fence."

"Get back to the postmen."

"They were just ordinary postmen, fond of walking
and dogs and Christmas and the snow.
They knocked on the doors with blue knuckles...."

"Ours has got a black knocker...."

"And then they stood on the white Welcome mat in
the little, drifted porches and huffed and puffed,
making ghosts with their breath, and jogged from
foot to foot like small boys wanting to go out."

"And then the Presents?"

"And then the Presents, after the Christmas box.
And the cold postman, with a rose on his
button-nose, tingled down the tea-tray-slithered run
of the chilly glinting hill. He went in his ice-bound
boots like a man on fishmonger's slabs. He wagged his
bag like a frozen camel's hump, dizzily turned the corner
on one foot, and, by God, he was gone."

"Get back to the Presents."

"There were the Useful Presents: engulfing mufflers
of the old coach days, and mittens made for giant
sloths; zebra scarfs of a substance like silky gum
that could be tug-o'-warred down to the galoshes;
blinding tam-o'-shanters like patchwork tea cosies
and bunny-suited busbies and balaclavas for victims
of head-shrinking tribes; from aunts who always
wore wool next to the skin there were moustached and
rasping vests that made you wonder why the aunts
had any skin left at all; and once I had a little
crocheted nose bag from an aunt now, alas,
no longer whinnying with us. And pictureless books
in which small boys, though warned with quotations
not to, *would* skate on Farmer Giles' pond
and did and drowned; and books that told me
everything about the wasp, except why."

"Go on to the Useless Presents."

"Bags of moist and many-coloured jelly babies
and a folded flag and a false nose and a tram-
conductor's cap and a machine that punched tickets
and rang a bell; never a catapult; once, by mistake
that no one could explain, a little hatchet;
and a celluloid duck that made, when you pressed it,
a most unducklike sound, a mewing moo that an
ambitious cat might make who wished to be a cow;
and a painting book in which I could make the grass,
the trees, the sea and the animals any colour
I pleased, and still the dazzling sky-blue sheep
are grazing in the red field under the
rainbow-billed and pea-green birds.
Hardboileds, toffee, fudge and allsorts, crunches,
cracknels, humbugs, glaciers, marzipan, and
butterwelsh for the Welsh. And troops of
bright tin soldiers who, if they could not fight,
could always run. And Snakes-and-Families

and Happy Ladders. And Easy Hobbi-Games
for Little Engineers, complete with instructions.
Oh, easy for Leonardo! And a whistle to make
the dogs bark to wake up the old man next door
to make him beat on the wall with his stick
to shake our picture off the wall.
And a packet of cigarettes: you put one
in your mouth and you stood at the corner
of the street and you waited for hours, in vain,
for an old lady to scold you for smoking
a cigarette, and then with a smirk you ate it.
And then it was breakfast under the balloons."

"Were there Uncles like in our house?"

"There are always Uncles at Christmas.
The same Uncles. And on Christmas mornings,
with dog-disturbing whistle and sugar fags,
I would scour the swatched town for the news of
the little world, and find always a dead bird
by the white Post Office or by the deserted swings;
perhaps a robin, all but one of his fires out.
Men and women wading or scooping back from chapel,
with taproom noses and wind-bussed cheeks,
all albinos, huddled their stiff black jarring
feathers against the irreligious snow.
Mistletoe hung from the gas brackets in all
the front parlours; there was sherry and walnuts
and bottled beer and crackers by the dessertspoons;
and cats in their fur-abouts watched the fires;
and the high-heaped fire spat, all ready for
the chestnuts and the mulling pokers.
Some few large men sat in the front parlours,
without their collars, Uncles almost certainly,
trying their new cigars, holding them out
judiciously at arms' length, returning them
to their mouths, coughing, then holding them out
again as though waiting for the explosion;
and some few small Aunts, not wanted in the kitchen,

nor anywhere else for that matter, sat on the
very edges of their chairs, poised and brittle,
afraid to break, like faded cups and saucers."

Not many those mornings trod the piling streets:
an old man always, fawn-bowlered, yellow-gloved
and, at this time of year, with spats of snow,
would take his constitutional to the white bowling
green and back, as he would take it wet or fine
on Christmas Day or Doomsday; sometimes two hale
young men, with big pipes blazing, no overcoats
and wind-blown scarfs, would trudge, unspeaking,
down to the forlorn sea, to work up an appetite,
to blow away the fumes, who knows, to walk
into the waves until nothing of them was left
but the two curling smoke clouds of their
inextinguishable briars. Then I would be
slap-dashing home, the gravy smell of the dinners
of others, the bird smell, the brandy, the
pudding and mince, coiling up to my nostrils, when
out of a snow-clogged side lane would come a boy
the spit of myself, with a pink-tipped cigarette
and the violet past of a black eye, cocky
as a bullfinch, leering all to himself.

I hated him on sight and sound, and would be
about to put my dog whistle to my lips
and blow him off the face of Christmas when
suddenly he, with a violet wink, put *his* whistle
to *his* lips and blew so stridently, so high,
so exquisitely loud, that gobbling faces,
their cheeks bulged with goose, would press
against their tinselled windows, the whole length
of the white echoing street. For dinner
we had turkey and blazing pudding, and after
dinner the Uncles sat in front of the fire,
loosened all buttons, put their large moist
hands over their watch chains, groaned a little
and slept. Mothers, aunts and sisters scuttled

to and fro, bearing tureens. Auntie Bessie, who
had already been frightened, twice, by a
clock-work mouse, whimpered at the sideboard
and had some elderberry wine. The dog was sick.
Auntie Dosie had to have three aspirins,
but Auntie Hannah, who liked port, stood in
the middle of the snowbound back yard, singing
like a big-bosomed thrush. I would blow up
ballons to see how big they would blow up to;
and, when they burst, which they all did,
the Uncles jumped and rumbled. In the rich
and heavy afternoon, the Uncles breathing
like dolphins and the snow descending,
I would sit among festoons and Chinese lanterns
and nibble dates and try to make a model man-o' war,
following the Instructions for Little Engineers,
and produce what might be mistaken for
a sea-going tramcar.

Or I would go out, my bright new boots
squeaking, into the white world, on to the
seaward hill, to call on Jim and Dan and Jack
and to pad through the still streets, leaving
huge deep footprints on the hidden pavements.

"I bet people will think there's been hippos."

"What would you do if you saw a hippo
coming down our street?"

"I'd go like this, bang! I'd throw him over
the railings and roll him down the hill and then
I'd tickle him under the ear and he'd wag his tail."

"What would you do if you saw *two* hippos?"

Iron-flanked and bellowing he-hippos clanked
and battered through the scudding snow toward us
as we passed Mr Daniel's house.

"Let's post Mr Daniel a snowball through
his letter-box."

"Let's write things in the snow."

"Let's write, 'Mr Daniel looks like a spaniel'
all over his lawn."

Or we walked on the white shore.
"Can the fishes see it's snowing?"

The silent one-clouded heavens drifted on to the sea.
Now we were snow-blind travellers lost on the
north hills, and vast dewlapped dogs, with flasks
round their necks, ambled and shambled up to us,
baying "Excelsior." We returned home through the
poor streets where only a few children fumbled
with bare red fingers in the wheel-rutted snow
and cat-called after us, their voices fading away,
as we trudged uphill, into the cries of the dock
birds and the hooting of ships out in the whirling
bay. And then, at tea the recovered Uncles would
be jolly; and the ice cake loomed in the centre of
the table like a marble grave. Auntie Hannah laced
her tea with rum, because it was only once a year.

Bring out the tall tales now that we told
by the fire as the gaslight bubbled like a diver.
Ghosts whooed like owls in the long nights

when I dared not look over my shoulder; animals
lurked in the cubbyhole under the stairs where the
gas meter ticked. And I remember that we went
singing carols once, when there wasn't the shaving
of a moon to light the flying streets. At the end
of a long road was a drive that led to a large
house, and we stumbled up the darkness of the drive
that night, each one of us afraid, each one holding
a stone in his hand in case, and all of us too brave
to say a word. The wind through the trees
made noises as of old and unpleasant and maybe
webfooted men wheezing in caves. We reached
the black bulk of the house.

"What shall we give them? Hark the Herald?"

"No," Jack said, "Good King Wenceslas.
I'll count three."

One, two, three, and we began to sing,
our voices high and seemingly distant in the
snow-felted darkness round the house that
was occupied by nobody we knew. We stood
close together, near the dark door.

Good King Wenceslas looked out
On the Feast of Stephen…

And then a small, dry voice, like the voice
of someone who has not spoken for a long time,
joined our singing: a small, dry, eggshell voice
from the other side of the door: a small dry voice
through the keyhole. And when we stopped running
we were outside *our* house; the front room was lovely;
balloons floated under the hot-water-bottle-gulping gas;
everything was good again and shone over the town.

"Perhaps it was a ghost," Jim said.

"Perhaps it was trolls," Dan said,
who was always reading.

"Let's go in and see if there's any jelly left,"
Jack said. And we did that.

Always on Christmas night there was music.
An uncle played the fiddle, a cousin sang
"Cherry Ripe," and another uncle sang "Drake's Drum."
It was very warm in the little house.
Auntie Hannah, who had got on to the parsnip
wine, sang a song about Bleeding Hearts and Death,
and then another in which she said her heart
was like a Bird's Nest; and then everybody
laughed again; and then I went to bed.
Looking through my bedroom window, out into
the moonlight and the unending smoke-coloured snow,
I could see the lights in the windows
of all the other houses on our hill and hear
the music rising from them up the long, steadily
falling night. I turned the gas down, I got
into bed. I said some words to the close and
holy darkness, and then I slept.

Hoodoo McFiggan's Christmas

by
STEPHEN LEACOCK
(1869–1944)

"Hoodoo McFiggan's Christmas" is probably Stephen Leacock's most popular Christmas story, and one which listeners always enjoy. Hoodoo—wherever does he get these names?—is a boy who plays the Christmas game most faithfully, being at all times a good and generous-minded boy. What is it to Hoodoo that others are more cynical? What is it to Hoodoo that others do not share in his delight?

T his Santa Claus business is played out. It's a sneaking, underhand method, and the sooner it's exposed the better.

For a parent to get up under cover of the darkness of night and palm off a ten-cent necktie on a boy who had been expecting a ten-dollar watch, and then say that an angel sent it to him, is low, undeniably low.

I had a good opportunity of observing how the thing worked this Christmas, in the case of young Hoodoo McFiggin, the son and heir of the McFiggins, at whose house I board.

Hoodoo McFiggin is a good boy—a religious boy. He had been given to understand that Santa Claus would bring nothing to his father and mother because grown-up people don't get presents from the angels. So he saved up all his pocket money and bought a box of cigars for his father and a seventy-five cent diamond brooch for his mother. His own fortunes he left in the hands of the angels. But he prayed. He prayed every night for weeks that Santa Claus would bring him a pair of skates and a puppy-dog and an air-gun and a bicycle and a Noah's ark and a sleigh and a drum—altogether about a hundred and fifty dollars' worth of stuff.

I went into Hoodoo's room quite early Christmas morning. I had an idea that the scene would be interesting. I woke him up and he sat up in bed, his eyes glistening with radiant expectation, and began hauling things out of his stocking.

The first parcel was bulky; it was done up quite loosely and had an odd look generally.

"Ha! ha!" Hoodoo cried gleefully, as he began undoing it. "I'll bet it's the puppy-dog, all wrapped up in paper!"

And was it the puppy-dog? No, by no means. It was a pair of nice, strong, number-four boots, laces and all, labelled, "Hoodoo, from Santa Claus," and underneath Santa Claus had written, "95 net."

The boy's jaw fell with delight. "It's boots," he said, and plunged in his hand again.

He began hauling away at another parcel with renewed hope on his face.

This time the thing seemed like a little round box. Hoodoo tore the paper off it with a feverish hand. He shook it; something rattled inside.

"It's a watch and chain! It's a watch and chain!" he shouted. Then he pulled the lid off.

And was it a watch and chain? No. It was a box of nice, brand-new celluloid collars, a dozen of them all alike and all his own size.

The boy was so pleased that you could see his face crack up with pleasure.

He waited a few minutes until his intense joy subsided. Then he tried again.

This time the packet was long and hard. It resisted the touch and had a sort of funnel shape.

"It's a toy pistol!" said the boy, trembling with excitement. "Gee! I hope there are lots of caps with it! I'll fire some off now and wake up father."

No, my poor child, you will not wake your father with that. It is a useful thing, but it needs not caps and it fires no bullets, and you cannot wake a sleeping man with a tooth-brush. Yes, it was a tooth-brush—a regular beauty, pure bone all through, and ticketed with a little paper, "Hoodoo, from Santa Claus."

Again the expression of intense joy passed over the boy's face, and the tears of gratitude started from his eyes. He wiped them away with his tooth-brush and passed on.

The next packet was much larger and evidently contained

something soft and bulky. It had been too long to go into the stocking and was tied outside.

"I wonder what this is," Hoodoo mused, half afraid to open it. Then his heart gave a great leap, and he forgot all his other presents in the anticipation of this one. "It's the drum, all wrapped up!"

Drum nothing! It was pants—a pair of the nicest little short pants—yellowish-brown short pants—with dear little stripes of colour running across both ways, and here again Santa Claus had written, "Hoodoo, from Santa Claus, one fort net."

But there was something wrapped up in it. Oh, yes! There was a pair of braces wrapped up in it, braces with a little steel sliding thing so that you could slide your pants up to your neck, if you wanted to.

The boy gave a dry sob of satisfaction. Then he took out his last present. "It's a book," he said, as he unwrapped it. "I wonder if it is fairy stories or adventures. Oh, I hope it's adventures! I'll read it all morning."

No, Hoodoo, it was not precisely adventures. It was a small family Bible. Hoodoo had now seen all his presents, and he arose and dressed. But he still had the fun of playing with his toys. That is always the chief delight of Christmas morning.

First he played with his tooth-brush. He got a whole lot of water and brushed all his teeth with it. This was huge.

Then he played with his collars. He had no end of fun with them, taking them all out one by one and swearing at them, and then putting them back and swearing at the whole lot together.

The next toy was his pants. He had immense fun there, putting them on and taking them off again, and then trying to guess which side was which by merely looking at them.

After that he took his book and read some adventures called "Genesis" till breakfast-time.

Then he went downstairs and kissed his father and mother. His father was smoking a cigar, and his mother had her new brooch on. Hoodoo's face was thoughtful, and a light seemed to have broken in upon his mind. Indeed, I think it altogether likely that next Christmas he will hang on to his own money and take chances on what the angels bring.

Papa's Story

A Scot's Christmas Story

by
GEORGE MACDONALD
(1824–1905)

A story for Christmas, rather than about Christmas, from the author of the children's classics, At the Back of the North Wind *and* The Princess and the Goblin. *As George MacDonald once wrote, "For my part, I do not write for children, but for the childlike, whether of five, or fifty, or seventy-five." "A Scot's Christmas Story" is the story of Nelly, a very grown-up child, and her brother Willie, a somewhat childish adult: and somewhere in between (probably just about the part where Jumper the dog comes in) there's a great deal of wisdom, and a lovely little tale to be told.*

213

"O tell us a story, papa," said a wise-faced little girl, one winter night as she intermitted for a moment her usual occupation of the hour before bed-time—that, namely, of sucking her thumb, earnestly and studiously followed, as if the fate of the world lay on the faithfulness of the process; "Do tell us a story, papa."

"Yes, do, papa," chimed in several more children. "It is *such* a long time since you told us a story."

"I don't think papa ever told us a story," said one of the youngest.

"Oh, Dolly!" exclaimed half a dozen. But her next elder sister took up the speech.

"Yes, I dare say. But you were only born last year, and papa has been away for months and months."

Now, Dolly was five, and her papa had been away for three weeks.

"Well," interposed their papa, "I will try. What shall it be about?"

"Oh! about Scotland," cried the eldest.

"Why do you want a story about Scotland?"

"Because you will like it best yourself, papa."

"I don't want one about Scotland. I'm not a Scotchman, though papa is," cried Dolly, "I'm an Englishman."

"I like Scotch stories," said the sucker of thumbs; "only I can't understand the curious words. They sound so rough, I never can understand them."

"Well, my darlings, I will tell you one about Scotland, and there shan't be a Scotch word in it. If one single one comes out of my mouth you may punish me anyway you please."

"Oh, that's jolly! How shall we punish papa if he says one Scotch word?"

"Pull his beard!" said Dolly.

"No, that would be rude!" cried three or four.

Whereupon Dolly's face changed, and she took to her thumb, like Katy.

"Make him pay a fine."

"That's no use, papa's so rich!"

Whereas the chief difficulty papa had in telling the story was the thought of the butcher's bill popping in through twenty different keyholes.

"Make him pay a kiss to each of us for every word!"

"No, that would stop the story!"

"Kiss him to death when it's done!"

"Yes!—yes!—yes—kiss him to death when it's done!"

So it was agreed; and papa began.

"You know, my darlings, there are a great many hills in Scotland, which are green with grass to the very top, and the sheep feed all over them?"

"Oh, yes! I know! Like Hampstead-hill."

"No. Like that place in the City—Ludgate-hill."

"No, my dears; not like either of those. Just come to the window, and I will try to show you. You see that star shining so brightly away there?"

"Yes. But that is not a hill, papa; it's a star!"

"Yes, it's a star. But suppose you could not see that star for a great heap of rock and earth and stone rising up between you and the star, covered with grass, and with streams of water running down its sides in every direction, that heap would be a hill. And in some parts of Scotland there are a great many of these hills crowded together, only divided from each other by deep places called valleys. They all grow out of one root—that is the earth. The tops of these hills are high up and lonely in the air, with the stars above them, and often the clouds round about them like torn garments."

"What's *garments*, Kitty?"

"Frocks, Dolly."

"What tears them, then?"

"The wind tears them; and goes roaring and raving about the hills; and makes such a noise against the steep rocks, running into the holes in them and out again, that those hills are sometimes very awful places. But in the sunshine, although they do look lonely, they are so bright and beautiful, that all the boys and girls fancy the way to heaven lies up those hills."

"And doesn't it?"

"No."

"Where is it, then?"

"Ah! that's just what you come here to find out. But you must let me go on with my story now. In the winter, on the other hand, they are such wild howling places, with the hard hailstones beating upon them, and the soft, smothering snowflakes heaping up dreadful wastes of whiteness upon them, that if ever there was a child out on them he would die with fear, if he did not die with cold. But there are only sheep there, and they don't stay very high up the hills when the winter once begins to come over the mountains."

"What's mountains?"

"Mountains are higher hills yet."

"Higher yet! They can't be higher yet."

"Oh! yes, they are; and there are higher and higher yet, till you could hardly believe it, even when you saw them.

"Well, as the winter comes over the tops of the hills the sheep come down their sides, because it is warmer the lower down you come; and even a foot thick of wool on their backs and sides could not keep out the terrible cold up there.

"But the sheep are not very knowing creatures, so they are something better instead. They are wise—that is, they are obedient—creatures, obedience being the very best wisdom. For, because they are not very knowing, they have a man to take care of them, who knows where to take them, especially when a storm comes on. Not that the sheep are so very silly as not to know where to go to get out of the wind, but they don't and can't think that some ways of getting out of danger are still more dangerous still. They would lie down in a quiet place, and lie there till the snow settled down over them and smothered them. They would not feel it cold, their wool is so thick. Or they would tumble down steep places and be killed, or buried in the snow, or carried away by the stream at the bottom. So, though they know a little, they don't know enough, and need a shepherd to take care of them.

"Now the shepherd, though he is wise, is not quite clever enough for all that is wanted of him up in those strange, terrible hills; and he needs another to help him. Now, who do you think helps the shepherd? Ah! you know, Maggy; but you mustn't tell. I will tell. It is a curious creature with four legs—the shepherd has only two, you know;—and he is covered all over with long hair of three different colours mixed—black, and brown, and white; and he has a long nose and a longer tongue, which he knows how to hold. This tongue it is a great comfort to him sometimes to hang out of his mouth as far as ever it will hang. And he has a still longer tail, which is a greater comfort to him yet. I don't know what ever he would do without his tail; for, when his master speaks kindly to him, he is so full of delight, that I think he would die if he hadn't his tail to wag. He lets his gladness off by wagging his tail, so that it shan't burst his dear, honest, good dog-heart. Ah! there, I've told you. He's a dog, you see; and the very wisest and cleverest of all dogs. He could be taught anything. Only he is such a gentleman, though dressed very plainly, as a great many gentlemen are, that it would be a shame to teach him some of the things they teach common-place rich dogs.

"Well, the shepherd tells the dog what he wants done, and off the dog runs to do it; for he can run three times as fast as the shepherd, and can get up and down places much better. I am not sure that he can see better than the shepherd, but I know he can smell better. So that he is just four legs and a long nose to the shepherd, besides the love he gives him, which would comfort any good man, even if it were offered him by a hedgehog or a hen. And for his understanding, if I were to tell Willie how much I believe he understands—if I weren't his papa, that is— Willie, there, who has such a high opinion of his own judgment, and shakes his head so knowingly when he hears anything for the first time, as if it were a shame for anything to come into existence without letting him know first—Willie, I say, would consider me silly for believing it, or, what would be a great deal worse, would think that I didn't really believe it, though I said it.

"One evening, in the beginning of April, the weakly sun of the season had gone down with a pale face behind the shoulder of a hill in the background of my story. If you had been there and had climbed up that hill, you would have seen him a great while longer, provided he had not, in the mean time, set behind a mountain of cloud, which, at this season of the year, he was very ready to do, and which, I suspect, he actually did this very evening about which I am telling you. And because he was gone down, the peat-fires upon the hearths of the cottages all began to glow more brightly, as if they were glad he was gone at last and had left them their work to do—or, rather, as if they wanted to do all they could to make up for his absence. And on one hearth in particular the peat-fire glowed very brightly. There was a pot hanging over it, with supper in it; and there was a little girl sitting by it, with a sweet, thoughtful face. Her hair was done up in a silken net, for it was the custom with Scotch girls—they wore no bonnet—to have their hair so arranged, many years before it became a fashion in London. She had a bunch of feathers, not in her hair, but fastened to her side by her apron-string, in the quill-ends of which was stuck the end of one of her knitting-needles, while the other was loose in her hand. But both were fast and busy in the loops of a blue-ribbed stocking, which she was knitting for her father.

"He was out on the hills. He had that morning taken his sheep higher up than before, and Nelly knew this; but it could not be long now till she would hear his footsteps, and measure the long stride between which brought him and happiness home together."

"But hadn't she any mother?"

"Oh! yes, she had. If you had been in the cottage that night you would have heard a cough every now and then, and would have found that Nelly's mother was lying in a bed in the room—not a bed with curtains, but a bed with doors like a press. This does not seem a nice way of having a bed; but we should all be glad of the wooden curtains about us at night if we lived in such a cottage, on the side of a hill along which the wind swept like a wild river, only ten times faster than any river would run even down the hillside. Through the cottage it would be spouting, and streaming, and eddying, and fighting, all night long; and a poor woman with a cough, or a man who has been out in the cold all day, is very glad of such a place to lie in, and leave the rest of the house to the wind and the fairies.

"Nelly's mother was ill, and there was little hope of her getting well again. What she could have done without Nelly, I can't think. It was so much easier to be ill with Nelly sitting there. For she was a good Nelly.

"After a while Nelly rose and put some peats on the fire, and hung the pot a link or two higher on the chain; for she was a wise creature, though she was only twelve, and could cook very well, because she took trouble, and thought about it. Then she sat down to her knitting again, which was a very frugal amusement.

"'I wonder what's keeping your father, Nelly,' said her mother from the bed.

"'I don't know, mother. It's not very late yet. He'll be home by and by. You know he was going over the shoulder of the hill to-day.'

"Now that was the same shoulder of the hill that the sun went down behind. And at the moment the sun was going down behind it, Nelly's father was standing on the top of it, and Nelly was looking up to the very place where he stood, and yet she did not see him. He was not too far off to be seen, but the sun was in her eyes, and the light of the sun hid him from her. He was then coming across with the sheep, to leave them for the night in a sheltered place—within a circle of stones that would keep the wind off them; and he ought, by rights, to have been home at least half an hour ago.—At length Nelly heard the distant sound of a heavy shoe upon the point of a great rock that grew up from the depths of the earth and just came through the surface in the path leading across the furze and brake to their cottage. She always watched for that sound—the sound of her father's shoe, studded thick with broad-headed nails, upon the top of that rock. She started up; but instead of rushing out to meet him, went to the fire and lowered the pot. Then taking up a wooden bowl, half full of oatmeal neatly pressed down into it, with a little salt on the top, she proceeded to make a certain dish for her father's supper, of which strong Scotchmen are very fond. By the time her father reached the door, it was ready, and set down with a plate over it to keep it hot, though it had a great deal more need, I think, to be let cool a little.

"When he entered, he looked troubled. He was a tall man, dressed in rough grey cloth, with a broad, round, blue bonnet, as they call it. His face looked as if it had been weatherbeaten into peace."

"Beaten into pieces, papa! How dreadful!"

"Be quiet, Dolly; that's not what papa means."

"I want to know, then."

"Well, Dolly, I think it would take twenty years at least to make it plain to you, so I had better go on with my story, especially as you will come to understand it one day without my explaining it. The shepherd's face, I say, was weatherbeaten and quiet, with large, grand features, in which the docility of his dogs and the gentleness of his sheep were mingled with the strength and wisdom of a man who had to care for both dogs and sheep.

"'Well, Nelly,' he said, laying his hand on her forehead as she looked up into his face, 'how's your mother?'

"And without waiting for an answer he went to the bed, where the pale face of his wife lay upon the pillow. She held out her thin, white hand to him, and he took it so gently in his strong, brown hand. But, before he had spoken, she saw the trouble on his face, and said,

"'What has made you so late to-night, John?'

"'I was nearly at the fold,' said the shepherd, 'before I saw that one of the lambs was missing. So, after I got them all in, I went back with the dogs to look for him.'

"'Where's Jumper, then?' asked Nelly, who had been patting the neck and stroking the ears of the one dog which had followed at the shepherd's heels, and was now lying before the fire, enjoying the warmth none the less that he had braved the cold all day without minding it a bit.

"'When we couldn't see anything of the lamb,' replied her

father, 'I told Jumper to go after him and bring him to the house; and Blackfoot and I came home together. I doubt he'll have a job of it, poor dog! for it's going to be a rough night; but if dog can bring him, he will.'

"As the shepherd stopped speaking, he seated himself by the fire and drew the wooden bowl towards him. Then he lifted his blue bonnet from his head, and said grace, half aloud, half murmured to himself. Then he put his bonnet on his head again, for his head was rather bald, and, as I told you, the cottage was a draughty place. And just as he put it on, a blast of wind struck the cottage and roared in the wide chimney. The next moment the rain dashed against the little window of four panes, and fell hissing into the peat-fire.

"'There it comes,' said the shepherd.

"'Poor Jumper!' said Nelly.

"'And poor little lamb!' said the shepherd.

"'It's the lamb's own fault,' said Nelly; 'he shouldn't have run away.'

"'Ah! yes,' returned her father; 'but then the lamb didn't know what he was about exactly.'

"When the shepherd had finished his supper, he rose and went out to see whether Jumper and the lamb were coming; but the dark night would have made the blackest dog and the whitest lamb both of one colour, and he soon came in again. Then he took the Bible and read a chapter to his wife and daughter, which did them all good, even though Nelly did not understand very much of it. And then he prayed a prayer, and was very near praying for Jumper and the lamb, only he could not quite. And there he was wrong. He should have prayed about whatever troubled him or could be done good to. But he was such a good man that I am almost ashamed of saying he was wrong.

"And just as he came to the *Amen* in his prayer, there came a whine to the door. And he rose from his knees and went and opened the door. And there was the lamb with Jumper behind him. And Jumper looked dreadfully wet, and draggled, and tired, and the curls had all come out of his long hair. And yet he seemed as happy as dog could be, and looked up in the face of the shepherd triumphantly, as much as to say, 'Here he is,

Master!' And the lamb looked scarcely anything the worse; for his thick, oily wool had kept away the wet; and he hadn't been running about everywhere looking for Jumper as Jumper had been for him.

"And Jumper, after Nelly had given him his supper, lay down by the fire beside the other dog, which made room for him to go next to the glowing peats; and the lamb, which had been eating all day and didn't want any supper, lay down beside him. And then Nelly bade her father and mother and the dogs good-night, and went away to bed likewise, thinking the wind might blow as it pleased now, for sheep and dogs, and father and all, were safe for the whole of the dark, windy hours between that and the morning. It is so nice to know that there is a long *nothing to do*;—but only after everything is done.

"But there are other winds in the world besides those which shake the fleeces of sheep and the beards of men, or blow ships to the bottom of the sea, or scatter the walls of cottages abroad over the hillsides. There are winds that blow up huge storms inside the hearts of men and women, and blow till the great clouds full of tears go up, and rain down from the eyes to quiet them."

"What can papa mean?"

"Never you mind, Dolly. You'll know soon enough. I'm fourteen, and I know what papa means."

"Nelly lay down in her warm bed, feeling as safe and snug as ever child felt in a large, rich house in a great city. For there was the wind howling outside to make it all the quieter inside; and there was the great, bare, cold hill before the window, which, although she could not see it, and only knew that it was there, made the bed in which she lay so close, and woolly, and warm. Now this bed was separated from her father and mother's only by a thin partition, and she heard them talking. And they had not talked long before that other cold wind that was blowing through their hearts blew into hers too. And I will tell you what they said to each other that made the cold wind blow into her heart.

"'It wasn't the loss of the lamb, John, that made you look so troubled when you came home to-night,' said her mother.

"'No, it wasn't, Jane, I must confess,' returned her father.

"'You've heard something about Willie.'

"'I can't deny it.'

"'What is it?'

"'I'll tell you in the morning.'

"'I shan't sleep a wink for thinking whatever it can be, John. You had better tell me now. If the Lord would only bring that stray lamb back to his fold, I should die happy—sorry as I should be to leave Nelly and you, my own John.'

"'Don't talk about dying, Jane. It breaks my heart.'

"'We won't talk about it, then. But what's this about Willie? And how came you to hear it?'

"'I was close to the hill-road, when I saw James Jamieson, the carrier, coming up the hill with his cart. I ran and met him.'

"'And he told you? What did he tell you?'

"'Nothing very particular. He only hinted that he had heard, from Wauchope the merchant, that a certain honest man's son— he meant me, Jane—was going the wrong road. And I said to James Jamieson—What road could the man mean? And James said to me—He meant the broad road, of course. And I sat down on a stone, and I heard no more; at least, I could not make sense of what James went on to say; and when I lifted my head, James and his cart were just out of sight over the top of the hill. I daresay that was how I lost the lamb.'

"A deep silence followed, and Nelly understood that her mother could not speak. At length a sob and a low weeping came through the boards to her keen mountain ear. But not another word was spoken; and, although Nelly's heart was sad, she soon fell fast asleep.

"Now, Willie had gone to college, and had been a very good boy for the first winter. They go to college only in winter in Scotland. And he had come home in the end of March and had helped his father to work their little farm, doing his duty well to the sheep and to everything and everybody; for learning had not made him the least unfit for work. Indeed, work that learning does really make a man unfit for, cannot be fit work for that man—perhaps is not fit work for anybody. When winter came, he had gone back to Edinburgh, and he ought to have been home a week ago, and he had not come. He had written to say that he had to finish some lessons he had begun to give, and could not be home till the end of the month. Now this was so far true that it was not a lie. But there was more in it: he did not want to go home to the lonely hillside—so lonely, that there were only a father and a mother and a sister there. He had made acquaintance with some students who were fonder of drinking whisky than of getting up in the morning to write abstracts, and he didn't want to leave them.

"Nelly was, as I have said, too young to keep awake because she was troubled; and so, before half an hour was over, was fast asleep and dreaming. And the wind outside, tearing at the thatch of the cottage, mingled with her dream.

"I will tell you what her dream was.—She thought they were out in the dark and the storm, she and her father. But she was no longer Nelly; she was Jumper. And her father said to her, 'Jumper, go after the black lamb and bring him home.' And away she galloped over the stones, and through the furze, and across the streams, and up the rocks, and jumped the stone fences, and swam the pools of water, to find the little black lamb. And all the time, somehow or other, the little black lamb was her brother Willie. And nothing could turn the dog Jumper, though the wind blew as if it would blow him off all his four legs, and off the hill, as one blows a fly off a book. And the hail beat in Jumper's face, as if it would put out his eyes or knock holes in his forehead, and yet Jumper went on."

"But it wasn't Jumper; it was Nelly, you know."

"I know that, but I am talking about the dog Jumper, that Nelly thought she was. He went on and on, and over the top of the cold wet hill, and was beginning to grow hopeless about finding the black lamb, when, just a little way down the other side, he came upon him behind a rock. He was standing in a miry pool, all wet with rain. Jumper would never have found him, the night was so dark and the lamb was so black, but that he gave a bleat; whereupon Jumper tried to say Willie, but could not, and only gave a gobbling kind of bark. So he jumped upon the lamb, and taking a mouthful of his wool, gave him a shake that made him pull his feet out of the mire, and then drove him off before him, trotting all the way home. When they came into the cottage, the black lamb ran up to Nelly's mother, and jumped into her bed, and Jumper jumped in after him; and then

Nelly was Nelly and Willie was Willie, as they used to be, when Nelly would creep into Willie's bed in the morning and kiss him awake. Then Nelly woke, and was sorry that it was a dream. For Willie was still away, far off on the broad road, and how ever was he to be got home? Poor black lamb!

"She soon made up her mind. Only how to carry out her mind was the difficulty. All day long she thought about it. And she wrote a letter to her father, telling him what she was going to do; and when she went to her room the next night, she laid the letter on her bed, and, putting on her Sunday bonnet and cloak, waited till they should be asleep.

"The shepherd had gone to bed very sad. He, too, had been writing a letter. It had taken him all the evening to write, and Nelly had watched his face while he wrote it, and seen how the muscles of it worked with sorrow and pain as he slowly put word after word down on the paper. When he had finished it, and folded it up, and put a wafer on it, and addressed it, he left it on the table, and, as I said, went to bed, where he soon fell asleep; for even sorrow does not often keep people awake that have worked hard through the day in the open air. And Nelly was watching.

"When she thought he was asleep, she took a pair of stockings out of a chest and put them in her pocket. Then, taking her Sunday shoes in her hand, she stepped gently from her room to the cottage door, which she opened easily, for it was never locked. She then found that it was pitch dark; but she could keep the path well enough, for her bare feet told her at once when she was going off it. It is a great blessing to have bare feet. People with bare feet can always keep the path better, and keep their garments cleaner, too. Only they must be careful to wash them at night.

"So, dark as it was, she soon reached the road. There was no wind that night, and the clouds hid the stars. She would turn in the direction of Edinburgh, and let the carrier overtake her. For she felt rather guilty, and was anxious to get on.

"After she had walked a good while, she began to wonder that the carrier had not come up with her. The fact was that the carrier never left till the early morning. She was not a bit afraid, though, reasoning that, as she was walking in the same direction, it would take him so much the longer to get up with her.

"At length, after walking a long way—far longer than she thought, for she walked a great part of it half asleep—she began to feel a little tired, and sat down upon a stone by the roadside. There was a stone behind her, too. She could just see its grey face. She leaned her back against it, and fell fast asleep.

"When she woke she could not think where she was, or how she had got there. It was a dark, drizzly morning, and her feet were cold. But she was quite dry. For the rock against which she fell asleep in the night projected so far over her head that it had kept all the rain off her. She could not have chosen a better place, if she had been able to choose. But the sight around her was very dreary. In front lay a swampy ground, creeping away, dismal and wretched, to the horizon, where a long low hill closed it. Behind her rose a mountain, bare and rocky, on which neither sheep nor shepherd was to be seen. Her home seemed to have vanished in the night, and left her either in a dream or in another world. And as she came to herself, the fear grew upon her that either she had missed the way in the dark or the carrier had gone past while she slept, either of which was dreadful to contemplate. She began to feel hungry, too, and she had not had the foresight to bring even a piece of oatcake with her.

"It was only dusky dawn yet. There was plenty of time. She would sit down again for a little while; for the rock had a home-ly look to her. It had been her refuge all night, and she was not willing to leave it. So she leaned her arms on her knees, and gazed out upon the dreary, grey, misty flat before her.

"Then she rose, and, turning her back on the waste, kneeled down, and prayed God that, as he taught Jumper to find lambs, he would teach her to find her brother. And thus she fell fast asleep again.

"When she woke once more and turned towards the road, whom should she see standing there but the carrier, staring at her. And his big strong horses stood in the road too, with their carts behind them. They were not in the least surprised. She could not help crying, just a little, for joy.

"'Why, Nelly, what on earth are you doing here?' said the carrier.

"'Waiting for you,' answered Nelly.

"'Where are you going, child?'

"'To Edinburgh.'

"'What on earth are you going to do in Edinburgh?'

"'I am going to my brother Willie, at the college.'

"'But the college is over now.'

"'I know that,' said Nelly.

"'What's his address, then?' the carrier went on.

"'I don't know,' answered Nelly.

"'It's a lucky thing that I know, then. But you have no business to leave home this way.'

"'Oh! yes, I have.'

"'I am sure your father did not know of it, for when he gave me a letter this morning to take to Willie he did not say a word about you.'

"'He thought I was asleep in my bed,' returned Nelly, trying to smile. But the thought that the carrier had actually seen her father since she left home was too much for her, and she cried.

"'I can't go back with you now,' said the carrier, 'so you must go on with me.'

"'That's just what I want,' said Nelly.

"So the carrier made her put on her shoes and stockings, for he was a kind man and had children of his own. Then he pulled out some of the straw that packed his cart, and made her a little bed on the tarpaulin that covered it, just where there was a soft bundle beneath. Then he lifted her up on it and covered her over with a few empty sacks. There Nelly was so happy, and warm, and comfortable, that, for the third time, she fell asleep.

"When she woke he gave her some bread and cheese for her breakfast, and some water out of a brook that crossed the road, and then Nelly began to look about her. The rain had ceased and the sun was shining, and the country looked very pleasant; but Nelly thought it a strange country. She could see so much farther! And corn was growing everywhere, and there was not a sheep to be seen, and there were many cows feeding in the fields.

"'Are we near Edinburgh?' she asked.

"'Oh, no!' answered the carrier; 'we are a long way from Edinburgh yet.'

"And so they journeyed on. The day was flecked all over with sunshine and rain; and when the rain's turn came, Nelly would creep under a corner of the tarpaulin till it was over. They slept part of the night at a small town they passed through.

"Nelly thought it a very long way to Edinburgh, though the carrier was kind to her, and gave her of everything that he had himself, except the whisky, which he did not think good for her.

"At length she spied, far away, a great hill, that looked like a couching lion.

"'Do you see that hill?' said the carrier.

"'I am just looking at it,' answered Nelly.

"'Edinburgh lies at the foot of that hill.'

"'Oh!' said Nelly; and scarcely took her eyes off it till it went out of sight again.

"Reaching the brow of an eminence, they saw Arthur's Seat (as the carrier said the hill was called) once more, and below it a great jagged ridge of what Nelly took to be broken rocks. But the carrier told her that was the Old Town of Edinburgh. Those fierce-looking splinters on the edge of the mass were the roofs, gables, and chimneys of the great houses once inhabited by the nobility of Scotland. But when you come near the houses you find them shabby-looking; for they are full of poor people, who cannot keep them clean and nice.

"But, certainly, my children, if you will excuse your Scotch papa for praising his own country's capital, I don't believe there ever was a city that looked so grand from the distance as that Old Town of Edinburgh. And when you get into the streets you can fancy yourself hundreds of years back in the story of Scotland. Seen thus through the perspective of time or distance, it is a great marvel to everyone with any imagination at all; and it was nothing less to little Nelly, even when she got into the middle of it. But her heart was so full of its dog-duties towards her black lamb of a brother that the toyshops and the sugar-plum-shops could not draw it towards their mines of wonder and wealth.

"At length the cart stopped at a public-house in the Grassmarket—a wide, open place, with strange old houses all round it, and a huge rock, with a castle on its top, towering over it. There Nelly got down.

"'I can't go with you till I've unloaded my cart,' said the carrier.

"'I don't want you to go with me, please,' said Nelly. 'I think Willie would rather not. Please give me father's letter.'

"So the carrier gave her the letter, and got a little boy of the landlady's to show her the way up the West-bow—a street of tall houses, so narrow that you might have shaken hands across it from window to window. But those houses are all pulled down now, I am sorry to say, and the street Nelly went up has vanished. From the West-bow they went up a stair into the High-street, and thence into a narrow court, and then up a winding stair, and so came to the floor where Willie's lodging was. There the little boy left Nelly.

"Nelly knocked two or three times before anybody came; and when at last a woman opened the door, what do you think the woman did the moment she inquired after Willie?—She shut the door in her face with a fierce scolding word. For Willie had vexed her that morning, and she thoughtlessly took her revenge upon Nelly without even asking her a question. Then, indeed, for a moment, Nelly's courage gave way. All at once she felt dreadfully tired, and sat down upon the stair and cried. And the landlady was so angry with Willie that she forgot all about the little girl that wanted to see him.

"So for a whole hour Nelly sat upon the stair, moving only to let people pass. She felt dreadfully miserable, but had not the courage to knock again, for fear of having the door shut in her face yet more hopelessly. At last a woman came up and knocked at the door. Nelly rose trembling and stood behind her. The door opened; the woman was welcomed; she entered. The door was again closing when Nelly cried out in agony.

"'Please, ma'am, I want to see my brother Willie!' and burst into sobs.

"The landlady, her wrath having by this time assuaged, was vexed with herself and ashamed that she had not let the child in.

"'Bless me!' she cried; 'have you been there all this time? Why didn't you tell me you were Willie's sister? Come in. You won't find him in, though. It's not much of his company we get, I can tell you.'

"'I don't want to come in, then,' sobbed Nelly. 'Please to tell me where he is, ma'am.'

"'How should I know where he is? At no good, I warrant. But you had better come in and wait, for it's your only chance of seeing him before to-morrow morning.'

"With a sore heart Nelly went in and sat down by the kitchen fire. And the landlady and her visitor sat and talked together, every now and then casting a look at Nelly, who kept her eyes on the ground, waiting with all her soul till Willie should come. Every time the landlady looked, she looked sooner the next time; and every time she looked, Nelly's sad face went deeper into her heart; so that, before she knew what was going on in herself, she quite loved the child; for she was a kind-hearted woman, though she was sometimes cross.

In a few minutes she went up to Nelly and took her bonnet off. Nelly submitted without a word. Then she made her a cup of tea; and while Nelly was taking it she asked her a great many questions. Nelly answered them all; and the landlady stared with amazement at the child's courage and resolution, and thought with herself,

"'Well, if anything can get Willie out of his bad ways, this little darling will do it.'

"Then she made her go to Willie's bed, promising to let her know the moment he came home.

"Nelly slept and slept till it was night. When she woke it was dark, but a light was shining through beneath the door. So she rose and put on her frock and shoes and stockings, and went to the kitchen.

"'You see he's not come yet, Nelly,' said the landlady.

"'Where can he be?' returned Nelly, sadly.

"'Oh! he'll be drinking with some of his companions in the public-house, I suppose.'

"'Where is the public-house?'

"'There are hundreds of them, child.'

"'I know the place he generally goes to,' said a young trades-man who sat by the fire.

"He had a garret-room in the house, and knew Willie by sight. And he told the landlady in a low voice where it was.

"'Oh! do tell me, please sir,' cried Nelly. 'I want to get him home.'

"'You don't think he'll mind you, do you?'

"'Yes, I do,' returned Nelly confidently.

"'Well, I'll show you the way if you like; but you'll find it a rough place, I can tell you. You'll wish yourself out of it pretty soon, with or without Willie.'

"'I won't leave it without him,' said Nelly, tying on her bonnet.

"'Stop a bit,' said the landlady. 'You don't think I am going to let the child out with nobody but you to look after her?'

"'Come along, then, ma'am.'

"The landlady put on her bonnet, and out they all went into the street.

"What a wonder it *might* have been to Nelly! But she only knew that she was in the midst of great lights, and carts and carriages rumbling over the stones, and windows full of pretty things, and crowds of people jostling along the pavements. In all the show she wanted nothing but Willie.

"The young man led them down a long dark close through an archway, and then into a court off the close, and then up an outside stone stair to a low-browed door, at which he knocked.

"'I don't much like the look of this place,' said the landlady.

"'Oh! there's no danger, I dare say, if you keep quiet. They never hurt the child. Besides, her brother'll see to that.'

"Presently the door was opened, and the young man asked after Willie.

"'Is he in?' he said.

"'He may be, or he may not,' answered a fat, frouzy woman, in a dirty cotton dress. 'Who wants him?'

"'This little girl.'

"'Please ma'am, I'm his sister.'

"'We want no sisters here.'

"And she proceeded to close the door. I dare say the landlady remembered with shame that that was just what she had done that morning.

"'Come! come!' interposed the young tradesman, putting his foot between the door and the post; 'don't be foolish. Surely you won't go to keep a child like that from speaking to her own brother! Why, the Queen herself would let her in.'

"This softened the woman a little, and she hesitated, with the latch in her hand.

"'Mother wants him,' said Nelly. 'She's very ill. I heard her cry about Willie. Let me in.'

"She took hold of the woman's hand, who drew it away hastily, but stepped back, at the same time, and let her enter. She then resumed her place at the door.

"'Devil a one of *you* shall come in!' she said, as if justifying the child's admission by the exclusion of the others.

"'We don't want, mistress,' said the young man. 'But we'll just see that no harm comes to her.'

"'D'ye think I'm not enough for that?' said the woman, with scorn. 'Let me see who dares to touch her! But you may stay where you are, if you like. The air's free.'

"So saying, she closed the door, with a taunting laugh.

"The passage was dark in which Nelly found herself; but she saw a light at the further end, through a keyhole, and heard the sounds of loud talk and louder laughter. Before the woman had closed the outer door, she had reached this room; nor did the woman follow either to guide or prevent her.

"A pause came in the noise. She tapped at the door.

"'Come in!' cried someone. And she entered.

"Round a table were seated four youths, drinking. Of them one was Willie, with flushed face and flashing eyes. They all stared when the child stood before them, in her odd, old-fashioned bonnet, and her little shawl pinned at the throat. Willie stared as much as any of them.

"Nelly spoke first.

"'Willie! Willie!' she cried, and would have rushed to him, but the table was between.

"'What do you want here, Nelly? Who the deuce let you come here?' said Willie, not quite unkindly.

"'I want you, Willie. Come home with me. Oh! please come home with me.'

"'I can't, now, Nelly, you see,' he answered. Then, turning to his companions, 'How could the child have found her way here?' he said, looking ashamed as he spoke.

"'You're fetched. That's all,' said one of them, with a sneer. 'Mother's sent for you.'

"'Go along!' said another; 'and mind you don't catch it when you get home!'

"'Nobody will say a word to you, Willie,' interposed Nelly.

"'Be a good boy, and don't do it again!' said the third, raising his glass to his lips.

"Willie tried to laugh, but was evidently vexed.

"'What are you standing there for, Nelly?' he said, sharply. 'This is no place for you.'

"'Not for you either, Willie,' returned Nelly, without moving.

"'We're all very naughty, aren't we, Nelly?' said the first.

"'Come and give me a kiss, and I'll forgive you,' said the second.

"'You shan't have your brother; so you may trudge home again without him,' said the third.

"And then they all burst out laughing, except Willie.

"'Do go away, Nelly,' he said, angrily.

"'Where am I to go to?' she asked.

"'Where you came from.'

"'That's home,' said Nelly; 'but I can't go home to-night, and I daren't go home without you. Mother would die. She's very ill, Willie. I heard her crying last night.'

"It seemed to Nelly at the moment that it was only last night she left home.

"'I'll just take the little fool to my lodgings and come back directly,' said Willie, rather stricken at this mention of his mother.

"'Oh! yes. Do as you're bid!' they cried, and burst out laughing again. For they despised Willie because he was only a shepherd's son, although they liked to have his company because he was clever. But Willie was angry now.

"'I tell you what,' he said, 'I'll go when and where I like.'

"Two of them were silent now, because they were afraid of Willie; for he was big and strong. The third, however, trusting to the others, said, with a nasty sneer,

"'Go with its little sister to its little mammy!'

"Now Willie could not get out, so small was the room and so large the table, except one or other of those next him rose to let him pass. Neither did. Willie therefore jumped on the table, kicked the tumbler of the one who had last spoken into the breast of his shirt, jumped down, took Nelly by the hand, and left the house.

"'The rude boys!' said Nelly. 'I would never go near them again, if I was you, Willie.'

"But Willie said never a word, for he was not pleased with Nelly, or with himself, or with his *friends*.

"When they got into the house he said, abruptly, 'What's the matter with mother, Nelly?'

"'I don't know, Willie; but I don't think she'll ever get better. I'm sure father doesn't think it either.'

"Willie was silent for a long time. Then he said,

"'How did you come here, Nelly?'

"And Nelly told him the whole story.

"'And now you'll come home with me, Willie.'

"'It was very foolish of you, Nelly. To think you could bring me home if I didn't choose!'

"'But you do choose, don't you, Willie?'

"'You might as well have written,' he said.

"Then Nelly remembered her father's letter, which the carrier had given her. And Willie took it, and sat down, with his back to Nelly, and read it through. Then he burst out crying, and laid his head on his arms and went on crying. And Nelly got upon a bar of the chair—for he was down on the table—and leaned over him, and put her arms round his neck, and said, crying herself all the time,

"'Nobody said a word to the black lamb when Jumper brought him home, Willie.'

"And Willie lifted his head, and put his arms round Nelly, and drew her face to his, and kissed her as he used to kiss her years ago.

"And I needn't tell you anything more about it."

"Oh! yes. Tell us how they got home."

"They went home with the carrier the next day."

"And wasn't his father glad to see Willie?"

"He didn't say much. He held out his hand with a half smile on his mouth, and a look in his eye like the moon before a storm."

"And his mother?"

"His mother held out her arms, and drew him down to her bosom, and stroked his hair, and prayed God to bless Willie, her boy."

"And Nelly—weren't they glad to see Nelly?"

"They made more of Willie than they did of Nelly."

"And wasn't Nelly sorry?"

"No; she never noticed it—she was so busy making much of Willie too."

"But I hope they didn't scold Nelly for going to fetch Willie?"

"When she went to bed that night, her father kissed her and said,

"'The blessin' o' an auld father be upo' ye, my wee bairn!'"

"There's Scotch," now exclaimed the whole company.

And in one moment papa was on the floor, buried beneath a mass of children.

The chief thumbsucker, after kissing till she was stupid, recovered her wits by sucking her thumb diligently for a whole minute, after which she said, "If we had been wolves, it would have been dangerous, papa."

And then they all went to bed.

The
Three Low Masses
A Christmas Tale

by
ALPHONSE DAUDET
(1840–1897)

One of Daudet's comic little masterpieces, "The Three Low Masses" is one of the funniest and dearest little stories that I can think of. Poor Father Balaguère! Who has not suffered the torments of the dreaded kitchen?—*that devil's den of human appetites. Who has not wished that a sermon or service (or some such thing) might somehow come to a speedy end—fini— so that we are free to pursue some less exalted goal just a little bit sooner? Poor Father Balaguère. Poor you. Poor me.*

I

"Two truffled turkeys, Garrigou?"

"Yes, your Reverence, two magnificent turkeys stuffed with truffles. I know, because I helped stuff them. The skin had been stretched so tightly you would have thought it was going to burst as it was roasting…"

"Jesus-Maria! How I do love truffles! Give me my surplice. Quickly, Garrigou… And what else did you see in the kitchen, besides the turkeys?…"

"Oh, all sorts of good things… Since midday they've done nothing but pluck pheasants, larks, pullets, grouse. Feathers flying everywhere… Then they brought eels, carp, trout from the pond and…"

"How big—the trout, Garrigou?"

"As big as that, your Reverence… Enormous!"

"Merciful heavens! You make me see them… Have you put the wine in the altar-cruets?"

"Yes, your Reverence, I've put the wine in the altar-cruets . . . But you wait and see! It doesn't compare with what you'll be drinking soon, after Midnight Mass. You should see inside the dining-room at the château: decanters blazing bright with wines of all colours… And the silver dishes, the carved dining-table, the flowers, the candelabra!… Never will there be a Christmas midnight supper like it. Monsieur le Marquis has invited all the nobility of the neighbourhood. You will be at least forty at table, not counting the bailiff and the scrivener. Ah, you are indeed fortunate to be among them, your Reverence! Just from having sniffed those beautiful turkeys, the smell of the truffles is following me everywhere… Myum!…"

"Come now, my son. Let us guard ourselves against the sin of gluttony, especially on the eve of the Nativity… Off with you, quickly. Light the candles and ring the bell for the first Mass; it is nearly midnight already, and we mustn't be late…"

This conversation took place one Christmas Eve in the year of grace sixteen hundred and something, between the Reverend Father Balaguère, formerly Prior of the Barnabites, at present Chaplain to the Lords of Trinquelage, and his little clerk Garrigou, for you must know that the devil, on that very evening, had assumed the round face and nondescript features of the young sacristan, the better to lead the reverend father into temptation and make him commit the terrible sin of gluttony. So, whilst the supposed Garrigou (Hem! hm!) was vigorously jingling the bells of the baronial chapel, the reverend father was hastening to clothe himself in his chasuble in the little sacristy of the château and, already troubled in spirit by all these gastronomic descriptions, he was repeating to himself as he dressed,

"Roast turkeys…golden carp…trout as big as that!…"

Outside, the night wind was blowing, spreading the music of the bells, and gradually lights were appearing in the darkness along the slopes of Mont Ventoux, on the top of which rose the age-old towers of Trinquelage. The families of the tenant-farmers were coming to hear Midnight Mass at the château. They sang as they climbed the incline in groups of five or six, the father in front, lantern in hand, the women swathed in their long, brown cloaks under which the children huddled for shelter. In spite of the hour and the cold, all these good folk walked cheerfully, sustained by the thought that when they came out from Mass there would be tables laid for them down in the kitchens, as there were every year. Now and then, on the steep slope, a nobleman's carriage preceded by torch bearers would twinkle its windows in the moonlight, or a mule would trot along tinkling its bells, and by the light of the mist-enveloped lanterns, the tenants would recognize their bailiff and salute him as he passed.

"Good evening, good evening, Master Arnoton!"

"Good evening, good evening, friends!"

The night was clear, the stars gleamed bright in the cold air; the north wind and a fine frozen snow, glancing off the clothes without wetting them, faithfully maintained the tradition of a white Christmas. At the very summit of the slope rose their destination, the château, with its enormous mass of towers and gables, its chapel spire rising into the bluish-black sky, and, at all its windows, little lights that twinkled, bobbing back and forth, and looking, against the dark background of the building, like sparks flashing in the ashes of burnt paper… Once one was beyond the draw-bridge of the postern-gate, to reach the chapel it was necessary to cross the outer courtyard, full of carriages, valets and sedan chairs, all brightly lit by the flames of torches and by the blazing kitchen fires. All around could be heard the chinking click of the turnspits, the clatter of pans, the clink of crystal and silver being set out in preparation for a feast; from up above, a warm vapour which smelt of roast meat and potent herbs used for complicated sauces made not only the tenants, but the chaplain, the bailiff, everybody, say:

"What a fine Christmas supper we are going to have after Mass!"

II

Dingdong-dong!… Dingdong-dong!…

So the Midnight Mass begins. In the chapel of the château, a cathedral in miniature, with interlaced arches and oak wainscoting high up the walls, tapestries have been hung, all the candles lit. And the people! The costumes! See first, seated in the carved stalls surrounding the chancel, the Lord of Trinquelage, in salmon-coloured taffeta, and near him all the invited nobility. Opposite, kneeling on prie-Dieus hung with velvet, are the old Dowager Marchioness in her gown of flame-coloured brocade and the young Lady of Trinquelage, wearing on her head the latest fashion of the Court of France: a high tower of fluted lace. Further back, their faces shaved, and wearing black with vast pointed wigs, can be seen the bailiff Thomas Arnoton and the scrivener Master Ambroy, striking two solemn notes among the gaudy silks and brocaded damasks. Then come the fat majordo-mos, the pages, the grooms, the stewards, the housekeeper with all her keys hung at her side on a fine silver chain. Further back, on benches, are the servants, the maids, and the tenants with their families. And last of all, at the very back, right against the door which they open and shut discreetly, are the scullions who slip in, between sauces, to snatch a little of the atmosphere of the Mass and to bring the smell of the supper into the church, festive and warm with all its lighted candles.

Is it the sight of the scullions' little white caps which distracts the officiating priest? Might it not rather be Garrigou's little bell, that mocking little bell which shakes at the foot of the altar with such infernal haste and seems to keep saying:

"Let's hurry! Let's hurry! The sooner we're finished, the sooner we'll be at supper."

The fact is that each time this devilish little bell rings, the chaplain forgets his Mass and thinks only of the midnight sup-per. He imagines the scurrying cooks, the kitchen stoves blazing like blacksmiths' forges, the steam escaping from half-open lids, and, beneath that steam, two magnificent turkeys, stuffed, taut, bursting with truffles…

Or still more, he sees pages passing in files carrying dishes surrounded with tempting odours, and he goes with them into the great hall already prepared for the feast. Oh, paradise! He sees the immense table blazing with lights and laden from end to end with peacocks dressed in their feathers, pheasants spreading their wings, flagons the colour of rubies, fruit daz-zling bright among green branches, and all the marvellous fish Garrigou was talking about (yes!—Garrigou, of course) dis-played on a bed of fennel, their scales pearly as if just from the sea, with bunches of sweet-smelling herbs in their huge nostrils. So real is the vision of these marvels that it seems to Father Balaguère that all these wonderful dishes are served before him on the embroidered altar-cloth, and once—or twice, instead of "*Dominus vobiscum!*" he catches himself saying "*Benedicite.*" Apart from these slight mistakes, the worthy man recites his office most conscientiously, without missing a line, without omitting one genuflection, and all goes very well until the end of the first Mass; for, as you know, the same priests must celebrate three consecutive Masses on Christmas Day.

"One over!" says the chaplain to himself with a sigh of relief; then, without wasting a moment, he signs to his clerk, or him whom he thinks is his clerk, and—

Dingdong-dong!... Dingdong-dong!...

So the second Mass begins, and with it begins also the sin of Father Balaguère.

"Quick, quick, let's hurry!" Garrigou's little bell cries to him in its shrill little voice, and this time the unfortunate priest abandons himself completely to the demon of gluttony, hurls himself on the missal and devours the pages with the avidity of his over-stimulated appetite. Frantically he kneels, rises, makes vague signs of the cross, half-genuflects, cuts short all his gestures in order to finish the sooner. He scarcely extends his arms at the Gospel, or beats his breast at the *Confiteor*. It is between the clerk and himself who will jabber the quicker. Verses and responses patter pell-mell, buffeting each other. Words half-pronounced without opening the mouth, which would take too much time, die away in a baffling hum.

"*Oremus ps...ps...ps...*"

"*Mea culpa...pa...pa...*"

Like hurrying wine-harvesters treading the grapes, both splatter about in the latin of the Mass, sending splashes in all directions.

"*Dom...scum!...,*" says Balaguère.

"*...Stutuo...,*" replies Garrigou; and all the time that damned little bell is ringing in their ears, like those bells they put on post-horses to make them gallop quicker. Obviously at this pace a Low Mass is quickly got out of the way.

"Two over!" says the chaplain quite out of breath; then, red and sweating, without pausing to recover, he rushes down the altar steps and...

Ding-dong!... Dingdong-dong!...

So the third Mass begins. It is not far now to the dining hall; but, alas, the nearer the midnight supper approaches, the more the unfortunate Balaguère feels himself seized by a gluttonous madness of impatience. He even sees more distinctly the golden carp, the roast turkeys... There!... Yes, and there!... He touches them...he... Oh, merciful heavens!...the dishes are steaming, the wines are ambrosial, and, shaking itself madly, the little bell is shrieking at him:

"Quick, quick! Be more quick!"

But how could he go more quickly? His lips are scarcely moving. He is no longer pronouncing the words… Unless he cheats the good God completely and omits part of the Mass… And that is exactly what the wretched man does! Falling deeper into temptation, he begins by skipping one verse, then two. Then the Epistle is too long so he doesn't finish it; he skims through the Gospel, passes over the Creed, jumps the Pater, bows distantly to the Preface, and thus by leaps and bounds hurls himself into eternal damnation, closely followed by the infamous Garrigou (*vade, retro, Satanus!*) who cooperates splendidly, holding up his chasuble, turning the pages two at a time, knocking over the desks, upsetting the altar-cruets, and ceaselessly shaking that tiny little bell, louder and louder, quicker and quicker.

The startled faces of the congregation are a sight to behold! Obliged to join in a Mass conducted in dumb-show by a priest whose words they can't hear, some stand up as others are kneeling, or sit when others are rising. And every succeeding part of this extraordinary service results in a confused variety of postures on all the benches. The Star of the Nativity, journeying up there across the sky towards the little stable, paled with apprehension at the sight of such disorder.

"The priest is going too quickly…you can't keep up with him," the old Dowager grumbles, shaking her coif angrily.

Master Arnoton, his large steel spectacles on his nose, searches in his prayer-book, wondering where the deuce they are up to. But, on the whole, all these worthy folk are themselves also thinking of the supper, and are not sorry the Mass is going at top speed. And when Father

Balaguère, his face shining radiantly, turns towards the congregation and shouts at the top of his voice: "*Ite, missa est,*" the whole chapel replies, as one voice, with a "*Deo Gratias*" so merry and so lively you would have thought they were already at table responding to the first toast.

III

Five minutes later, all the nobles were taking their seats in the great hall, the chaplain in the midst of them. The château, bright with lights in every room, was reverberating with songs, shouts, laughter, uproar everywhere; and the venerable Father Balaguère was plunging his fork into the wing of the grouse, drowning remorse for his sin under floods of wine and rich meat gravy. The unfortunate holy man drank so much and ate so much, he died of a stroke that night without even having time to repent. In the morning, he arrived in heaven still all in a stupor after the night's feasting and I leave you to ponder over the reception he was given.

"Get out of My sight, you wicked Christian!" the Sovereign Judge, Master of us all, said to him. "Your lapse from virtue is so great it outweighs all the goodness of your life. You stole from Me a Midnight Mass. Well, you will pay it back three-hundred-fold. You will not enter Paradise until you have celebrated three hundred Christmas Masses in your own chapel and in the presence of all those who sinned with you and by your fault."

…Such, in truth, is the legend of Father Balaguère, as you will hear it told in the land of olives. Today the Château de Trinquelage no longer exists, but the chapel still stands on the summit of Mont Ventoux, in a clump of holly oaks. Its disjointed door bangs in the wind, its threshold is overgrown with weeds; there are nests in the corners of the altar and in the recesses of the huge casement windows from which the coloured glass has long since disappeared. Yet it is said that at Christmas every year a supernatural light hovers among these ruins, and that peasants, going to Mass and the midnight supper in the church since built below, see this ghost of a chapel lit with invisible candles which burn in the open air even in wind and snow. You may laugh if you will, but a local vine-grower named Garrigue, a descendant no doubt of Garrigou, has assured me that one Christmas Eve, being slightly drunk, he had lost his way on the mountain near Trinquelage; and this is what he saw... Until eleven o'clock, nothing. Suddenly, towards midnight, a peal of bells sounded high in the steeple, an old peal not heard for many many years and seeming to come from many leagues away. Soon after, on the path leading upwards, Garrigue saw lights flickering, faint shadows moving. Under the chapel porch there were footsteps, voices whispering:

"Good evening, Master Arnoton!"

"Good evening, good evening, friends!"

When everyone had entered, my vine-grower, who was very brave, approached softly, looked through the broken door, and saw a strange sight. All these people he had seen passing were ranged in rows around the chancel, in the ruined nave, as if the ancient benches were still there. Beautiful ladies in brocade with coifs of lace, handsome noblemen bedecked from head to foot, peasants in flowered jackets such as our grandfathers wore; everything appeared faded, dusty, old and tired. From time to time night birds, the residents now of the chapel, woken by all the lights, came swooping around the candles whose flames burned erect yet nebulous, as if hidden behind a thin veil. And what amused Garrigue greatly was a certain person wearing large steel spectacles who kept shaking his tall black wig on which one of these birds stood, entangled, silently flapping its wings...

At the far end, a little old man no taller than a child was kneeling in the centre of the chancel, shaking despairingly a little, tongueless, soundless bell; while a priest clothed in old gold moved back and fro before the altar reciting prayers no word of which could be heard... It was, most surely, Father Balaguère saying his third Low Mass.

Réveillon Tourtière

and *The*

Morton Thompson Turkey

After the story of "The Three Low Masses" seems a fitting place to gather together two of my favourite Christmas recipes. The tourtière is a savory meat and pastry dish prepared especially to tempt the poor Father. The Morton Thompson turkey is nothing short of sinful. I first prepared the MT turkey one Thanksgiving at the cottage. It was a beautiful day: the sun was shining, there were family and friends (all taking turns basting the turkey and stuffing the stuffing). The more hands the better. The American novelist Morton Thompson spent years trying to convince readers that his recipe wasn't a joke. Pierre Berton gave me the recipe, and Pierre says if you try it make sure to leave nothing out: "the balance of spices is a delicate one. And do not neglect to baste your bird; that is half the battle."

Réveillon Tourtière

In Quebec, there is a name for the joyous Christmas Eve of feasting, gifts, dancing, storytelling and games that follow midnight mass. It's Réveillon, the time for families to gather together and rekindle warm traditions around a table laden with holiday dishes. Tourtière, a lightly spiced and herbed pork filling in a flaky pastry, is at the heart of Réveillon festivities.

1	tbsp	vegetable oil
2	lb	ground pork
1-1/2	cups	beef stock
3		onions, finely chopped
3		cloves garlic, minced
2	cups	sliced mushrooms
1	cup	finely chopped celery
3/4	tsp	salt
1/2	tsp	each cinnamon, pepper and dried savory
1/4	tsp	ground cloves
1	cup	fresh bread crumbs
1/2	cup	chopped fresh parsley
		Pastry for 9-inch double-crust pie
1		egg, beaten
1	tsp	water

In large skillet, heat oil over medium-high heat; cook pork, breaking up with wooden spoon, for 7 to 10 minutes or until no longer pink. Drain off fat.

Stir in stock, onions, garlic, mushrooms, celery, salt, cinnamon, pepper, savory and cloves; bring to boil. Reduce heat to medium-low and simmer, stirring occasionally, for 35 to 45 minutes or until 2 tbsp liquid remains.

Stir in fresh bread crumbs and parsley. Taste and adjust seasoning if necessary. Cover and refrigerate until cold or for up to 1 day.

On lightly floured surface, roll out bottom pastry to 1/8-inch thickness; fit into 9-inch pie plate.

Spoon filling into pie shell, smoothing top. Roll out top pastry. Moisten rim of pie shell with water. Cover with top pastry, pressing edges together to seal. Trim and flute pastry edge.

Combine egg and water; brush some over pastry. Cut decorative shapes from remaining pastry and arrange on top; brush with some of the remaining egg mixture.

Cut steam vents in top; bake in 375° oven for 40 to 45 minutes or until golden brown. Let cool for 10 minutes. Makes 8 to 10 servings.

The Morton Thompson Turkey

1 turkey (up to 25 pounds), with neck, heart, gizzard, and liver

Dressing, Bowl #1:

       1 apple, peeled, cored, and sliced
       1 orange, peeled and sectioned
       1/2 lemon, peeled and sectioned
       1 26-ounce can water chestnuts
       3 tbsp. fresh or preserved ginger
       1 26-ounce can crushed pineapple

Dressing, Bowl #2:

       4 cloves
       2 tsp. dry English mustard
       2 tsp. caraway seeds
       3 tsp. celery seeds
       2 tsp. poppy seeds
       2 1/2 tsp. oregano
       1 bay leaf, crushed
       1 tsp. black pepper
       1/2 tsp. mace
       4 tbsp. fresh parsley, chopped
       5 cloves garlic, chopped
       1/2 tsp. turmeric
       4 large onions, chopped
       6 stalks celery, chopped
       1/2 tsp. marjoram
       1/2 tsp. savory
       1 tbsp. poultry seasoning
       Salt to taste

Dressing, Bowl #3:

       Fat from turkey
       3 11-ounce packages
         breadcrumbs
       3/4 pound ground veal
       1/4 pound ground pork
       1/2 cup butter

Basting fluid and gravy:

> 1 bay leaf
> 1 tsp. paprika
> 1/2 tsp. ground coriander
> 1 clove garlic, chopped
> 4 cups water
> Salt and pepper to taste
> 1 cup apple cider

Paste cover:

> 8 egg yolks
> 2 tbsp. dry English mustard
> 1/4 cup onion juice
> 2 tsp. salt
> 1/2 tsp. cayenne pepper
> 2 tbsp. lemon juice
> Sifted flour

1. Mix all Bowl #1 ingredients thoroughly.
2. Mince cloves after discarding the heads. Mix all Bowl #2 ingredients thoroughly.
3. In a small skillet, render as much fat as possible from the turkey. Mix fat in a bowl with other ingredients from Bowl #3.
4. Mix together all the dressing bowls. "Mix it until your forearms and wrists ache," Thompson wrote. "Then mix it some more. Now toss it enough so it isn't a doughy mass."
5. Chop up the turkey's neck, heart, gizzard, and liver. Place in a saucepan with bay leaf, paprika, coriander, garlic, and water. (Do not add the cider at this point.) Simmer. The longer you simmer this basting fluid, the better. Keep adding water.
6. We make our dressing the night before and simmer our basting fluid all night. If you do that, however, keep the stuffing cool overnight.
7. Rub the bird inside and out with salt and pepper and stuff it reasonably full at both ends. Sew it up, or skewer it and tie

the ends. Tie the legs and wings tightly to the body with good strong cord.

8. Place bird on a rack, or place breast-side down on a drip pan. Put in 450° oven.

9. Mix together the ingredients for the paste cover. Sift in enough flour to make a stiff paste. As soon as the turkey is browned all over from the red-hot oven, haul it out, sizzling. Using a pastry brush, cover it completely with paste. Slip it back into the oven so that the paste will set. Then haul it out again and, in Thompson's words, "paint every nook and cranny of it once more."

10. Turn the oven down to 325°; put some water in the drip pan, and roast the turkey. The paste will keep the heat in. Never cook the turkey more than nine or ten minutes to the pound.

11. Add the cider to the giblet gravy simmering on the stove. Keep it warm. This is your basting fluid. You should baste the turkey thoroughly every 15 minutes. We use an aluminum baster with a rubber bulb, and we set the timer on the stove alarm to remind us when to baste. And don't forget to keep adding water to the gravy in the pan to keep it from burning.

12. When you remove the turkey from the oven it will be dead black. Don't let that worry you. You can remove the paste, if you want, with tweezers, but we don't bother because beneath that shell the bird will be, in Thompson's words, "succulent, giddy-making with wild aroma, crisp and crunchable and crackling."

13. The gravy in the pan can be thickened with a little flour and cooked on top of the stove. We serve the turkey with bread sauce as well as cranberry sauce. As Thompson wrote: "You do not have to be a carver to eat this turkey; speak harshly to it and it will fall apart."

Markheim

by
ROBERT LOUIS STEVENSON
(1850–1894)

One dark tale for a stormy Christmas night. Robert Louis Stevenson's "Markheim" plays upon the Hyde side of the Christmas Jekyll—the hidden side of human suffering. I have chosen this story quite knowingly, for Christmas can also be a time of personal crisis, and it is important to recognize Markheim's plight—to see that what is needed, perhaps especially throughout the Christmas season, but for all the year, is human generosity and understanding. But, there, I am moralizing, something that Stevenson himself would never allow.

"Yes," said the dealer, "our windfalls are of various kinds. Some customers are ignorant, and then I touch a dividend on my superior knowledge. Some are dishonest," and here he held up the candle, so that the light fell strongly on his visitor, "and in that case," he continued, "I profit by my virtue."

Markheim had but just entered from the daylight streets, and his eyes had not yet grown familiar with the mingled shine and darkness in the shop. At these pointed words, and before the near presence of the flame, he blinked painfully and looked aside.

The dealer chuckled. "You come to see me on Christmas Day," he resumed, "when you know that I am alone in my house, put up my shutters, and make a point of refusing business. Well, you will have to pay for that; you will have to pay for my loss of time, when I should be balancing my books; you will have to pay, besides, for a kind of manner that I remark in you today very strongly. I am the essence of discretion, and ask no awkward questions; but when a customer cannot look me in the eye, he has to pay for it." The dealer once more chuckled; and then, changing to his usual business voice, though still with a note of irony, "You can give, as usual, a clear account of how you came into the possession of the object?" he continued. "Still your uncle's cabinet? A remarkable collector, sir!"

And the little pale, round-shouldered dealer stood almost on tip-toe, looking over the top of his gold spectacles, and nodding his head with every mark of disbelief. Markheim returned his gaze with one of infinite pity, and a touch of horror.

"This time," said he, "you are in error. I have not come to sell, but to buy. I have no curios to dispose of; my uncle's cabinet is bare to the wainscot; even were it still intact, I have done well on the Stock Exchange, and should more likely add to it than otherwise, and my errand today is simplicity itself. I seek a Christmas present for a lady," he continued, waxing more fluent as he struck into the speech he had prepared; "and certainly I owe you every excuse for thus disturbing you upon so small a matter. But the thing was neglected yesterday; I must produce my little compliment at dinner; and, as you very well know, a rich marriage is not a thing to be neglected."

There followed a pause, during which the dealer seemed to weigh this statement incredulously. The ticking of many clocks among the curious lumber of the shop, and the faint rushing of the cabs in a near thoroughfare, filled up the interval of silence.

"Well, sir," said the dealer, "be it so. You are an old customer after all; and if, as you say, you have the chance of a good marriage, far be it from me to be an obstacle. Here is a nice thing for a lady now," he went on, "this hand-glass—fifteenth century, warranted; comes from a good collection, too; but I reserve the name, in the interests of my customer, who was just like yourself, my dear sir, the nephew and sole heir of a remarkable collector."

The dealer, while he thus ran on in his dry and biting voice, had stooped to take the object from its place; and, as he had done so, a shock had passed through Markheim, a start both of hand and foot, a sudden leap of many tumultuous passions to the face. It passed as swiftly as it came, and left no trace beyond a certain trembling of the hand that now received the glass.

"A glass," he said hoarsely, and then paused, and repeated it more clearly. "A glass? For Christmas? Surely not?"

"And why not?" cried the dealer. "Why not a glass?"

Markheim was looking upon him with an indefinable expression. "You ask me why not?" he said. "Why, look here—look in it—look at yourself! Do you like to see it? No! nor I—nor any man."

The little man had jumped back when Markheim had so suddenly confronted him with the mirror; but now, perceiving there was nothing worse on hand, he chuckled. "Your future lady, sir, must be pretty hard favoured," said he.

"I ask you," said Markheim, "for a Christmas present, and you give me this—this damned reminder of years, and sins and follies—this hand-conscience! Did you mean it? Had you a thought in your mind? Tell me. It will be better for you if you do. Come, tell me about yourself. I hazard a guess now, that you are in secret a very charitable man?"

The dealer looked closely at his companion. It was very odd. Markheim did not appear to be laughing; there was something in his face like an eager sparkle of hope, but nothing of mirth.

"What are you driving at?" the dealer asked.

"Not charitable?" returned the other gloomily. "Not charitable; not pious; not scrupulous; unloving, unbeloved; a hand to get money, a safe to keep it. Is that all? Dear God, man, is that all?"

"I will tell you what it is," began the dealer, with some sharpness, and then broke off again into a chuckle. "But I see this is a love-match of yours, and you have been drinking the lady's health."

"Ah!" cried Markheim, with a strange curiosity. "Ah, have you been in love? Tell me about that."

"I," cried the dealer. "I in love! I never had the time, nor have I the time today for all this nonsense. Will you take the glass?"

"Where is the hurry?" returned Markheim. "It is very pleasant to stand here talking; and life is so short and insecure that I would not hurry away from any pleasure—no, not even from so mild a one as this. We should rather cling, cling to what little we can get, like a man at a cliff's edge. Every second is a cliff, if you think upon it—a cliff a mile high—high enough, if we fall, to dash us out of every feature of humanity. Hence it is best to talk pleasantly. Let us talk of each other: why should we wear this mask? Let us be confidential. Who knows, we might become friends?"

"I have just one word to say to you," said the dealer. "Either make your purchase, or walk out of my shop!"

"True, true," said Markheim. "Enough fooling. To business.

Show me something else."

The dealer stooped once more, this time to replace the glass upon the shelf, his thin blond hair falling over his eyes as he did so. Markheim moved a little nearer, with one hand in the pocket of his greatcoat; he drew himself up and filled his lungs; at the same time many different emotions were depicted together on his face—terror, horror, and resolve, fascination and a physical repulsion; and through a haggard lift of his upper lip, his teeth looked out.

"This, perhaps, may suit," observed the dealer: and then, as he began to re-arise, Markheim bounded from behind upon his victim. The long skewerlike dagger flashed and fell. The dealer struggled like a hen, striking his temple on the shelf, and then tumbled on the floor in a heap.

Time had some score of small voices in that shop, some stately and slow as was becoming to their great age; others garrulous and hurried. All these told out the seconds in an intricate chorus of tickings. Then the passage of a lad's feet, heavily running on the pavement, broke in upon these smaller voices and startled Markheim into the consciousness of his surroundings. He looked about him awfully. The candle stood on the counter, its flame solemnly wagging in a draught; and by that inconsiderable movement, the whole room was filled with noiseless bustle and kept heaving like a sea; the tall shadows nodding, the gross blots of darkness swelling and dwindling as with respiration, the faces of the portraits and the china gods changing and wavering like images in water. The inner door stood ajar, and peered into that leaguer of shadows with a long slit of daylight like a pointing finger.

From these fear-stricken rovings Markheim's eye returned to the body of his victim, where it lay both humped and sprawling, incredibly small and strangely meaner than in life. In these poor, miserly clothes, in that ungainly attitude, the dealer lay like so much sawdust. Markheim had feared to see it, and lo! it was nothing. And yet, as he gazed, this bundle of old clothes and pool of blood began to find eloquent voices. There it must lie; there was none to work the cunning hinges or direct the miracle of locomotion—there it must lie till it was found. Found! ay, and then? Then would his dead flesh lift up a cry that would ring over England, and fill the world with the echoes of pursuit. Ay, dead or not, this was still the enemy. "Time was that when the brains were out," he thought; and the first word struck into his mind. Time, now that the deed was accomplished—time, which had closed for the victim, had become instant and momentous for the slayer.

The thought was yet in his mind, when, first one and then another, with every variety of pace and voice—one deep as the bell from a cathedral turret, another ringing on its treble notes the prelude of a waltz—the clocks began to strike the hour of three in the afternoon.

The sudden outbreak of so many tongues in that dumb chamber staggered him. He began to bestir himself, going to and fro with the candle, beleaguered by moving shadows, and startled to the soul by chance reflections. In many rich mirrors, some of home design, some from Venice or Amsterdam, he saw his own face repeated and repeated, as it were an army of spies; his own eyes met and detected him; and the sound of his own steps, lightly as they fell, vexed the surrounding quiet. And still, as he continued to fill his pockets, his mind accused him with a sickening iteration of the thousand faults of his design. He should have chosen a more quiet hour; he should have prepared an alibi; he should not have used a knife; he should have been more cautious and only bound and gagged the dealer, and not killed him; he should have been more bold and killed the servant also; he should have done all things otherwise; poignant regrets, weary, incessant toiling of the mind to change what was unchangeable, to plan what was now useless, to be the architect of the irrevocable past. Meanwhile, and behind all this activity, brute terrors, like the scurrying of rats in a deserted attic, filled the more remote chambers of his brain with riot; the hand of the constable would fall heavy on his shoulder, and his nerves would jerk like a hooked fish; or he beheld, in galloping defile, the dock, the prison, the gallows, and the black coffin.

Terror of the people in the street sat down before his mind like a besieging army. It was impossible, he thought, but that some rumour of the struggle must have reached their ears and set on edge their curiosity; and now, in all the neighbouring houses, he divined them sitting motionless and with uplifted ear—solitary people, condemned to spend Christmas dwelling alone on memories of the past, and now startlingly recalled from that tender exercise; happy family parties, struck into silence round the table, the mother still with raised finger: every degree and age and humour, but all, by their own hearths, prying and hearkening and weaving the rope that was to hang him. Sometimes it seemed to him he could not move too softly; the clink of the tall Bohemian goblets rang out loudly like a bell; and alarmed by the bigness of the ticking, he was tempted to stop the clocks. And then, again, with a swift transition of his terrors, the very silence of the place appeared a source of peril, and a thing to strike and freeze the passer-by; and he would step more boldly, and bustle aloud among the contents of the shop and imitate, with elaborate bravado, the movements of a busy man at ease in his own house.

But he was now so pulled about by different alarms that, while one portion of his mind was still alert and cunning, another trembled on the brink of lunacy. One hallucination in particular took a strong hold on his credulity. The neighbour hearkening with white face beside his window, the passer-by arrested by a horrible surmise on the pavement—these could at worst suspect, they could not know; through the brick walls and shuttered windows only sounds could penetrate. But here, within the house, was he alone? He knew he was; he had watched the servant set forth sweethearting, in her poor best, "out for the day" written in every ribbon and smile. Yes, he was alone, of course; and yet, in the bulk of empty house above him, he could surely hear a stir of delicate footing—he was surely conscious, inexplicably conscious of some presence. Ay, surely; to every room and corner of the house his imagination followed it; and now it was a faceless thing, and yet had eyes to see with; and again it was a shadow of himself; and yet again behold the image of the dead dealer, reinspired with cunning and hatred.

At times, with a strong effort, he would glance at the open door which still seemed to repel his eyes. The house was tall, the skylight small and dirty, the day blind with fog; and the light that filtered down to the ground storey was exceedingly faint, and showed dimly on the threshold of the shop. And yet, in that strip of doubtful brightness, did there not hang wavering a shadow?

Suddenly, from the street outside, a very jovial gentleman began to beat with a staff on the shop door, accompanying his blows with shouts and railleries in which the dealer was continually called upon by name. Markheim, smitten into ice, glanced at the dead man. But no! he lay quite still; he was fled away far beyond earshot of these blows and shoutings; he was sunk beneath seas of silence; and his name, which would once have caught his notice above the howling of a storm, had become an empty sound. And presently the jovial gentleman desisted from his knocking and departed.

Here was a broad hint to hurry what remained to be done, to get forth from this accusing neighbourhood, to plunge into a bath of London multitudes, and to reach, on the other side of day, that haven of safety and apparent innocence—his bed. One visitor had come: at any moment another might follow and be more obstinate. To have done the deed, and yet not to reap the profit, would be too abhorrent a failure. The money, that was now Markheim's concern; and as a means to that, the keys.

He glanced over his shoulder at the open door, where the shadow was still lingering and shivering; and with no conscious repugnance of the mind, yet with a tremor of the belly, he drew near the body of his victim. The human character had quite departed. Like a suit half-stuffed with bran, the limbs lay scattered, the trunk doubled, on the floor; and yet the thing repelled him. Although so dingy and inconsiderable to the eye, he feared it might have more significance to the touch. He took the body by the shoulders and turned it on its back. It was strangely light and supple, and the limbs, as if they had been broken, fell into the oddest postures. The face was robbed of all expression; but it was as pale as wax, and shockingly smeared with blood about one temple. That was, for Markheim, the one displeasing circumstance. It carried him back, upon the instant, to a certain fair-day in a fishers' village: a grey day, a piping wind, a crowd upon the street, the blare of brasses, the booming of drums, the nasal voice of a ballad singer; and a boy going to and fro, buried over head in the crowd and divided between interest and fear, until, coming out on the chief place of concourse, he beheld a booth and a great screen with pictures, dis-

mally designed, garishly coloured: Brownrigg with her appren-
tice; the Mannings with their murdered guest; Weare in the
death-grip of Thurtell; and a score besides of famous crimes.
The thing was as clear as an illusion; he was once again that little boy; he was looking once again, with the same sense of physical revolt, at these vile pictures; he was still stunned by the
thumping of the drums. A bar of that day's music returned upon
his memory; and at that, for the first time, a qualm came over
him, a breath of nausea, a sudden weakness of the joints, which
he must instantly resist and conquer.

He judged it more prudent to confront than to flee from these
considerations; looking the more hardily in the dead face, bending his mind to realise the nature and greatness of his crime. So
little a while ago that face had moved with every change of sentiment, that pale mouth had spoken, that body had been all on
fire with governable energies; and now, and by his act, that
piece of life had been arrested, as the horologist, with interjected
finger, arrests the beating of the clock. So he reasoned in vain;
he could rise to no more remorseful consciousness; the same
heart which had shuddered before the painted effigies of crime,
looked on its reality unmoved. At best, he felt a gleam of pity for
one who had been endowed in vain with all those faculties that
can make the world a garden of enchantment, one who had
never lived and who was now dead. But of penitence, no, not a
tremor.

With that, shaking himself clear of these considerations, he
found the keys and advanced towards the open door of the
shop. Outside, it had begun to rain smartly; and the sound of
the shower upon the roof had banished silence. Like some dripping cavern, the chambers of the house were haunted by an
incessant echoing, which filled the ear and mingled with the
ticking of the clocks. And, as Markheim approached the door,
he seemed to hear, in answer to his own cautious tread, the
steps of another foot withdrawing up the stair. The shadow still
palpitated loosely on the threshold. He threw a ton's weight of
resolve upon his muscles, and drew back the door.
The faint, foggy daylight glimmered dimly on the bare floor

and stairs; on the bright suit of armour posted, halbert in hand, upon the landing; and on the dark wood-carvings and framed pictures that hung against the yellow panels of the wainscot. So loud was the beating of the rain through all the house, that, in Markheim's ears, it began to be distinguished into many different sounds. Footsteps and sighs, the tread of regiments marching in the distance, the chink of money in the counting, and the creaking of doors held stealthily ajar, appeared to mingle with the patter of drops upon the cupola and the gushing of the water in the pipes. The sense that he was not alone grew upon him to the verge of madness. On every side he was haunted and begirt by presences. He heard them moving in the upper chambers; from the shop, he heard the dead man getting to his legs; and as he began with a great effort to mount the stairs, feet fled quietly before him and followed stealthily behind. If he were but deaf, he thought, how tranquilly he would possess his soul! And then again, and hearkening with ever fresh attention, he blessed himself for that unresting sense which held the outposts and stood a trusty sentinel upon his life. His head turned continually on his neck; his eyes, which seemed starting from their orbits, scouted on every side, and on every side were half-rewarded as with the tail of something nameless vanishing. The four-and-twenty steps to the first floor were four-and-twenty agonies.

On that first storey the doors stood ajar, three of them like three ambushes, shaking his nerves like the throats of cannon. He could never again, he felt, be sufficiently immured and fortified from men's observing eyes; he longed to be home, girt in by walls, buried among bedclothes, and invisible to all but God. And at that thought he wondered a little, recollecting tales of other murderers and the fear they were said to entertain of heavenly avengers. It was not so, at least, with him. He feared the laws of nature, lest in their callous and immutable procedure they should preserve some damning evidence of his crime. He feared tenfold more, with a slavish, superstitious terror, some scission in the continuity of man's experience, some wilful illegality of nature. He played a game of skill, depending on the rules, calculating consequence from cause; and what if nature, as the defeated tyrant overthrew the chessboard, should break the mould of their succession? The like had befallen Napoleon (so writers said) when the winter changed the time of its appearance. The like might befall Markheim; the solid walls might become transparent and reveal his doings like those of bees in a glass hive; the stout planks might yield under his foot like quicksands and detain him in their clutch; ay, and there were soberer accidents that might destroy him; if, for instance, the house should fall and imprison him beside the body of his victim; or the house next door should fly on fire, and the firemen invade him from all sides. These things he feared; and, in a sense, these things might be called the hands of God reached forth against sin. But about God Himself he was at ease; his act was doubtless exceptional, but so were his excuses, which God knew; it was there, and not among men, that he felt sure of justice.

When he had got safe into the drawing-room and shut the door behind him, he was aware of a respite from alarms. The room was quite dismantled, uncarpeted besides, and strewn with packing-cases and incongruous furniture; several great pier-glasses, in which he beheld himself at various angles, like an actor on a stage; many pictures, framed and unframed, standing, with their faces to the wall; a fine Sheraton sideboard, a cabinet of marquetry, and a great old bed, with tapestry hangings. The windows opened to the floor; but by great good fortune the lower part of the shutters had been closed, and this concealed him from the neighbours. Here, then, Markheim drew in a packing-case before the cabinet and began to search among the keys. It was a long business, for there were many, and it was irksome, besides; for, after all, there might be nothing in the cabinet, and time was on the wing. But the closeness of the occupation sobered him. With the tail of his eye he saw the door—even glanced at it from time to time directly, like a besieged commander pleased to verify the good estate of his defences. But in truth he was at peace. The rain falling in the street sounded natural and pleasant. Presently, on the other side, the notes of a piano were wakened to the music of a hymn, and the voices of many children took up the air and words. How stately, how comfortable was the melody! How fresh the youthful voices! Markheim gave ear to it smilingly, as he sorted out the keys; and his mind was thronged with answerable ideas and images; church-going children and the pealing of the high organ; children afield, bathers by the brookside, ramblers on the brambly common, kite-fliers in the windy and cloud-navigated sky; and then, at another cadence of the hymn, back again to church, and the somnolence of summer Sundays, and the high genteel voice of the parson (which he smiled a little to recall), and the painted Jacobean tombs, and the dim lettering of the Ten Commandments in the chancel.

And as he sat thus, at once busy and absent, he was startled to his feet. A flash of ice, a flash of fire, a bursting gush of blood, went over him, and then he stood transfixed and thrilling. A step mounted the stair slowly and steadily, and presently a hand was laid upon the knob, the lock clicked, and the door opened.

Fear held Markheim in a vice. What to expect he knew not, whether the dead man walking, or the official ministers of human justice, or some chance witness blindly stumbling in to consign him to the gallows. But when a face was thrust into the aperture, glanced round the room, looked at him, nodded and smiled as if in friendly recognition, and then withdrew again, and the door closed behind it, his fear broke loose from his control in a hoarse cry. At the sound of this the visitant returned.

"Did you call me?" he asked pleasantly, and with that he entered the room and closed the door behind him.

Markheim stood and gazed at him with all his eyes. Perhaps there was a film upon his sight, but the outlines of the newcomer seemed to change and waver like those of the idols in the wavering candlelight of the shop; and at times he thought he knew him; and at times he thought he bore a likeness to himself; and always, like a lump of living terror, there lay in his bosom the conviction that this thing was not of the earth and not of God.

And yet the creature had a strange air of the commonplace, as he stood looking on Markheim with a smile; and when he added: "You are looking for the money, I believe?" it was in the tones of everyday politeness.

Markheim made no answer.

"I should warn you," resumed the other, "that the maid has

left her sweetheart earlier than usual and will soon be here. If Mr Markheim be found in this house, I need not describe to him the consequences."

"You know me?" cried the murderer.

The visitor smiled. "You have long been a favourite of mine," he said; "and I have long observed and often sought to help you."

"What are you?" cried Markheim: "the Devil?"

"What I may be," returned the other, "cannot affect the service I propose to render you."

"It can," cried Markheim; "it does! Be helped by you? No, never; not by you! You do not know me yet; thank God, you do not know me!"

"I know you," replied the visitant, with a sort of kind severity or rather firmness. "I know you to the soul."

"Know me!" cried Markheim. "Who can do so? My life is but a travesty and slander on myself. I have lived to belie my nature. All men do; all men are better than this disguise that grows about and stifles them. You see each dragged away by life, like one whom bravos have seized and muffled in a cloak. If they had their own control—if you could see their faces, they would be altogether different, they would shine out for heroes and saints! I am worse than most; myself is more overlaid; my excuse is known to me and God. But, had I the time, I could disclose myself."

"To me?" inquired the visitant.

"To you before all," returned the murderer. "I supposed you were intelligent. I thought—since you exist—you would prove a reader of the heart. And yet you would propose to judge me by my acts! Think of it; my acts! I was born and I have lived in a land of giants; giants have dragged me by the wrists since I was born out of my mother—the giants of circumstance. And you would judge me by my acts! But can you not look within? Can you not understand that evil is hateful to me? Can you not see within me the clear writing of conscience, never blurred by any wilful sophistry, although too often disregarded? Can you not read me for a thing that surely must be common as humanity—the unwilling sinner?"

"All this is very feelingly expressed," was the reply, "but it regards me not. These points of consistency are beyond my province, and I care not in the least by what compulsion you may have been dragged away, so as you are but carried in the right direction. But time flies; the servant delays, looking in the faces of the crowd and at the pictures on the hoardings, but still she keeps moving nearer; and remember, it is as if the gallows itself was striding towards you through the Christmas streets! Shall I help you; I, who know all? Shall I tell you where to find the money?"

"For what price?" asked Markheim.

"I offer you the service for a Christmas gift," returned the other.

Markheim could not refrain from smiling with a kind of bitter triumph. "No," said he, "I will take nothing at your hands; if I were dying of thirst, and it was your hand that put the pitcher to my lips, I should find the courage to refuse. It may be credulous, but I will do nothing to commit myself to evil."

"I have no objection to a death-bed repentance," observed the visitant.

"Because you disbelieve their efficacy!" Markheim cried.

"I do not say so," returned the other; "but I look on these things from a different side, and when the life is done my interest falls. The man has lived to serve me, to spread black looks under colour of religion, or to sow tares in the wheatfield, as you do, in a course of weak compliance with desire. Now that he draws so near to his deliverance, he can add but one act of service—to repent, to die smiling, and thus to build up in confidence and hope the more timorous of my surviving followers. I am not so hard a master. Try me. Accept my help. Please yourself in life as you have done hitherto; please yourself more amply, spread your elbows at the board; and when the night begins to fall and the curtains to be drawn, I tell you, for your greater comfort, that you will find it even easy to compound your quarrel with your conscience, and to make a truckling peace with God. I came but now from such a death-bed, and the room was full of sincere mourners, listening to the man's last words: and when I looked into that face, which had been set as a flint against mercy, I found it smiling with hope."

"And do you, then, suppose me such a creature?" asked

Markheim. "Do you think I have no more generous aspirations than to sin, and sin, and sin, and, at the last, sneak into heaven? My heart rises at the thought. Is this, then, your experience of mankind? or is it because you find me with red hands that you presume such baseness? and is this crime of murder indeed so impious as to dry up the very springs of good?"

"Murder is to me no special category," replied the other. "All sins are murder, even as all life is war. I behold your race, like starving mariners on a raft, plucking crusts out of the hands of famine and feeding on each other's lives. I follow sins beyond the moment of their acting; I find in all that the last conse-quence is death; and to my eyes, the pretty maid who thwarts her mother with such taking graces on a question of a ball, drips no less visibly with human gore than such a murderer as your-self. Do I say that I follow sins? I follow virtues also; they differ not by the thickness of a nail, they are both scythes for the reap-ing angel of Death. Evil, for which I live, consists not in action but in character. The bad man is dear to me; not the bad act, whose fruits, if we could follow them far enough down the hurtling cataract of the ages, might yet be found more blessed than those of the rarest virtues. And it is not because you have killed a dealer, but because you are Markheim, that I offer to forward your escape."

"I will lay my heart open to you," answered Markheim. "This crime on which you find me is my last. On my way to it I have learned many lessons; itself is a lesson, a momentous lesson. Hitherto I have been driven with revolt to what I would not; I was a bond-slave to poverty, driven and scourged. There are robust virtues that can stand in these temptations; mine was not so: I had a thirst of pleasure. But today, and out of this deed, I pluck both warning and riches—both the power and a fresh resolve to be myself. I become in all things a free actor in the world; I begin to see myself all changed, these hands the agents of good, this heart at peace. Something comes over me out of the past; something of what I have dreamed on Sabbath evenings to the sound of the church organ, of what I forecast when I shed tears over noble books, or talked, an innocent child, with my mother. There lies my life; I have wandered a few years, but now I see once more my city of destination."

"You are to use this money on the Stock Exchange, I think?" remarked the visitor; "and there, if I mistake not, you have already lost some thousands?"

"Ah," said Markheim, "but this time I have a sure thing."

"This time, again, you will lose," replied the visitor quietly.

"Ah, but I keep back the half!" cried Markheim.

"That also you will lose," said the other.

The sweat started upon Markheim's brow. "Well, then, what matter?" he exclaimed. "Say it be lost, say I am plunged again in poverty, shall one part of me, and that the worse, continue until the end to override the better? Evil and good run strong in me, haling me both ways. I do not love the one thing, I love all. I can conceive great deeds, renunciations, martyrdoms; and though I be fallen to such a crime as murder, pity is no stranger to my thoughts. I pity the poor; who knows their trials better than myself? I pity and help them; I prize love, I love honest laughter; there is no good thing nor true thing on earth but I love it from my heart. And are my vices only to direct my life, and my virtues to lie without effect, like some passive lumber of the mind? Not so; good, also, is a spring of acts."

But the visitant raised his finger. "For six-and-thirty years that you have been in this world," said he, "through many changes of fortune and varieties of humour, I have watched you steadily fall. Fifteen years ago you would have started at a theft. Three years back you would have blenched at the name of murder. Is there any crime, is there any cruelty or meanness, from which you still recoil?—five years from now I shall detect you in the fact! Downward, downward, lies your way; nor can anything but death avail to stop you."

"It is true," Markheim said huskily, "I have in some degree complied with evil. But it is so with all; the very saints, in the mere exercise of living, grow less dainty, and take on the tone of their surroundings."

"I will propound to you one simple question," said the other; "and as you answer, I shall read to you your moral horoscope. You have grown in many things more lax; possibly you do right to be so; and at any account, it is the same with all men. But granting that, are you in any one particular, however trifling, more difficult to please with your own conduct, or do you go in all things with a looser rein?"

"In any one?" repeated Markheim, with an anguish of consideration. "No," he added, with despair, "in none! I have gone down in all."

"Then," said the visitor, "content yourself with what you are, for you will never change; and the words of your part on this stage are irrevocably written down."

Markheim stood for a long while silent, and indeed it was the visitor who first broke the silence. "That being so," he said, "shall I show you the money?"

"And grace?" cried Markheim.

"Have you not tried it?" returned the other. "Two or three years ago, did I not see you on the platform of revival meetings, and was not your voice the loudest in the hymn?"

"It is true," said Markheim; "and I see clearly what remains for me by way of duty. I thank you for these lessons from my soul; my eyes are opened, and I behold myself at last for what I am."

At this moment the sharp note of the doorbell rang through the house; and the visitant, as though this were some concerted signal for which he had been waiting, changed at once in his demeanour.

"The maid!" he cried. "She has returned, as I forewarned you, and there is now before you one more difficult passage. Her master, you must say, is ill; you must let her in, with an assured but rather serious countenance—no smiles, no over-acting, and I promise you success! Once the girl within, and the door closed, the same dexterity that has already rid you of the dealer will relieve you of this last danger in your path. Thenceforward you have the whole evening—the whole night, if needful—to ransack the treasures of the house and to make good your safety. This is help that comes to you with the mask of danger. Up!" he cried; "up, friend; your life hangs trembling in the scales: up, and act!"

Markheim steadily regarded his counsellor. "If I be condemned to evil acts," he said, "there is still one door of freedom open—I can cease action. If my life be an ill thing, I can lay it down. Though I be, as you say truly, at the beck of every small temptation, I can yet, by one decisive gesture, place myself beyond the reach of all. My love of good is damned to barrenness; it may, and let it be! But I have still my hatred of evil; and from that, to your galling disappointment, you shall see that I can draw both energy and courage."

The features of the visitor began to undergo a wonderful and lovely change: they brightened and softened with a tender triumph, and, even as they brightened, faded and dislimned. But Markheim did not pause to watch or understand the transformation. He opened the door and went downstairs very slowly, thinking to himself. His past went soberly before him; he beheld it as it was, ugly and strenuous like a dream, random as chance-medley—a scene of defeat. Life, as he thus reviewed it, tempted him no longer; but on the farther side he perceived a quiet haven for his bark. He paused in the passage and looked into the shop, where the candle still burned by the dead body. It was strangely silent. Thoughts of the dealer swarmed into his mind as he stood gazing. And then the bell once more broke out into impatient clamour.

He confronted the maid upon the threshold with something like a smile.

"You had better go for the police," said he: "I have killed your master."

A
Puzzling
Christmas Gift

by

WARREN CLEMENTS

(1952–   )

Over the years The Globe and Mail *has printed a number of
Christmas stories and poems from its contributors and editors. I
gathered together a selection of these stories (with the help of the
people at* The Globe*) and "The Puzzling Christmas Gift" is the
one I have chosen to include. The trick, I suppose, is to see more
simply—to see the world through a child's eyes.*

Charles Arthur realized shortly before Christmas that he hadn't yet bought a present for his young niece, and wandered off to the store to find something suitable.

"I want the best you have," he told the clerk behind the counter, who eyed him coolly, pegged him as a $14.95 customer and handed him a small box. "This is our most popular puzzle," said the clerk. "A steal at $14.95."

At home, Charles Arthur felt the least he could do before delivering the present was to try it himself and make sure it worked, which, considering his aptitude for things mechanical, was a grueling enough test for any unsuspecting toy.

He pulled the puzzle out of the box and studied it for several minutes. It had 28 sides and 15 different colors and yielded up no clues. He pulled out the instructions. They were written in five languages, none of which Charles Arthur had encountered before.

"Charming," he said. "How can I solve a puzzle when I don't know what it's supposed to look like in the end, and don't know why it looks the way it does in the beginning?" He dropped it on the floor. It didn't bounce. He tried twisting it. Nothing moved. He held it up to the light. It was opaque.

"Perhaps you have to shake it in a special sequence," he thought. The puzzle said nothing.

The next morning Charles Arthur took the puzzle back to the

store and demanded to know its secret. The clerk looked at it and called over his manager. The manager looked at it and telephoned the company that made it. Nobody there knew what it was supposed to do; all the company did was drop it into boxes, they said, and send it off in time for Christmas.

"I'm sorry," said the clerk. "It must be one of these trick contraptions that only mathematical prodigies can figure out."

When he examined it more closely, Charles Arthur noticed a small hole cutting through one of the angles, and stuck a pin into the hole. Nothing happened. There was no squeal, no whirr, no grinding of machinery. He dipped the puzzle into a sinkful of water and waited for it to explode, or dissolve, or at least shed its paint. A few bubbles rose to the surface—but the puzzle remained intact. Charles Arthur scratched his head.

The park near his home was a magnet for wise and healthy individuals, and Charles Arthur walked up there to solicit advice. "Excuse me," he asked everyone who walked by his bench, "do you know how to solve this puzzle?" A man in a fur coat said it was an anagram and passed on. A group of teenagers said he was holding it the wrong way. A woman pushing her baby in a stroller thought it looked like Rubik's Cube, but couldn't explain why none of the parts moved. "It must be broken," she said.

A child walked by and Charles Arthur stopped him in desperation. "I've lost the instructions to this puzzle," he said, "and I wonder if you can help me." The child looked at the toy and then looked at Charles Arthur. "This isn't a puzzle," he said. "This is a tree ornament." And he walked away.

"It can't be a tree ornament," snapped the clerk when Charles Arthur broke the news to him, "We've sold 50,000 of these in three weeks as brain-teasing puzzles. Are you trying to tell me that 50,000 adults are wracking their brains trying to solve something which a child took three seconds to dismiss as a tree ornament?"

Charles Arthur admitted this was unlikely indeed, and took the puzzle home and mailed it to his small niece, who removed it from the packaging and hung it on the family Christmas tree and spent hours watching it turn, slowly one way and slowly the other, and had the merriest holiday imaginable.

Long Day's Journey into Prayer

by
CONOR CRUISE O'BRIEN
(1917–   )

The eternal Irish dilemma. If you sat in a pub somewhere in the west of Ireland you might overhear two workers having the most serious (and intimidatingly intelligent) conversation on some aspect of church matters. The church is not to be taken lightly in the Republic of Ireland, and Conor Cruise O'Brien touches all the right chords as a "Long Day's Journey into Prayer" moves toward a Christmas Day of thankfulness and recognition.

Just before last Christmas it so happened that I wanted to say a prayer. I stifled the temptation.

It came back, as temptations do. I found myself engaged in the following internal dialogue:—

"So you want to say a prayer? Why don't you get on with it, and stop annoying me?"

"I won't get on with it because I'm an agnostic."

"What's that got to do with it?"

"An agnostic is someone who doesn't believe in God."

"So what?"

"You can't say a prayer to someone you don't believe in."

"Why can't you?"

"Um."

My father had been an agnostic. We lived in Dublin. Agnosticism ran in the family, a bit: my mother's eldest sister and her son Owen were agnostics, too. All the rest were Catholics, traditional, Tridentine. My mother had tried being an agnostic, out of loyalty to my father. When he died she gave up and went back to being a Catholic. She also started to pray hard, very hard, even for an Irish Roman Catholic. She started praying on Christmas Night 1927. The reason why she started praying on that particular night was that my father died that morning, suddenly, of a heart attack, while bending a bow for me, my present from him.

You can forget about the bow. The important word, as any Roman Catholic reader sees instantly, is "suddenly."

There was no time to send for the priest. If there had been, my mother would most certainly have asked my father to send for him. And I believe he *would* have sent for him, mainly because he knew it would be a comfort to my mother and—therefore—to me. For the same sort of reason, James Joyce, another Dublin Catholic agnostic, but of much stricter obedience than my father, felt able to tell his little sister that their mother was in Heaven.

Being a *live* agnostic was not then—and is not now—taken very seriously in Ireland. Not very long ago a prominent Belfast Catholic revealed to his Parish Priest that he (the PBC) had become an agnostic. The man of God kept his cool: "You're not an agnostic, Paddy. You're just a fat slob who's too lazy to go to Mass."

But to be an agnostic *who had died without the priest* was, in 1927, and for years afterwards, a much more serious matter. Everybody we knew well was kind to my mother about this. They explained to my mother that my father would certainly go to Heaven, because he had "lived a good life." These reassurances were in themselves alarming. What my mother was worried about was not *whether* my father would go to Heaven—she took that for granted—but *when* he would get there.

The great question, in fact, was Purgatory, a thriving institution at the time. My mother did not believe—as a less educated widow in her position might have believed, and would have been *told*—that her husband was undergoing a course of physical torture somewhere under the earth. She believed that he might be "separated from God." It was not the separation from God that worried her: it was the separation from *her*. By her bedside I saw for the first time, in early January 1928, a manual of devotion: *In Heaven We Know Our Own* by Fr. Blot, S.J. I didn't need to read the book. The title was enough.

You see, to know your own in Heaven, your own have to get there, and I knew that the date of my father's arrival at that destination was problematical. The reason for that was myself. Because my father, besides being an agnostic, and dying without the priest, had done something much worse: he had sent me to a Protestant school, because he thought Protestant schools were better than Catholic ones, which they were.

My mother was told that if she prayed she could *shorten* my father's term in purgatory. So she prayed like mad. But she was also told that every term she kept me on at a Protestant school *lengthened* my father's term of suffering. She would not take me away from that school because it had been my father's wish that I should go there, and that was that. Every day of her life was shortening, lengthening, praying and holding firm, with heroic fortitude.

Years afterwards, a Pope decided that enough was enough, and closed Purgatory down. Of course, he said he *wasn't* closing the place down, it had just somehow never been there. It had been there all right, I knew, because my mother was shut up in it for more than ten years, from Christmas 1927 to her death at Easter 1938.

These transactions left me, naturally, with a dislike of the God about whose character, methods and punitive accountancy so much curious and precise information had been so pressingly conveyed to my mother. Dislike took the form of disbelief. The transition was very neatly expressed by my cousin, Owen— older and tougher and wittier than I—who, being asked by a clergyman why he considered that God didn't exist, made the gentle, wide-eyed answer: "Don't you think it's the most charitable hypothesis?"

That was the stuff to give them.

I was left with two other things: a kind of shiver recurring every Christmas Day, and a horror of prayer. The prayers I had been closest to were the cries of pain wrung from my mother by her spiritual tormentors. Think anyone was going to get one of *those* out of me? Not a prayer! But somebody did.

After a car accident, on 14 November last year, my wife was seriously ill in Jervis Street Hospital, Dublin. That hospital must be one of the best in the world; in the quality of its medical care and of its nursing and in constant personal kindness. It is run by nuns.

My wife is a practising Catholic. She asked people—not me—to pray for her, and they did. People asked me to tell her they were praying for her, and I did. People came up to me in the street and asked how she was. When I told them things were not so good, they said please God. When I told them things were getting better, they said thank God, and that a lot of people had been praying for her.

In the street conversations I did not re-echo the please God. But when it came to thanking God, I found myself repeating it all right. I felt a bit guilty about this, but, after all, they were decent people and it was only civil.

Things began to move from please God to thank God just before Christmas. On Christmas Day we knew for sure she was going to be all right. I brought in the children. We shared champagne and Coke with the nurses. Thank God spanged out on all sides. I joined in recklessly, not out of civility, but out of sheer joy. She was going to be all right. Thank God.

It didn't matter a damn whether I believed in God or not, or even whether I *wanted* to thank Him. I was just thanking Him anyway: and I noticed something.

The old shiver, inseparable from every Christmas Day over exactly half a century, had clean gone. I had often read "The Ancient Mariner," but that Christmas morning in St. Agnes Ward, I *was* that venerable seafarer. That damned bird had gone! There was nothing round my neck anymore!

The self-same moment I could pray.

Yes, Virginia, There is a Santa Claus

ANONYMOUS

"Yes, Virginia, There is a Santa Claus" appeared on the editorial page of the New York Sun, *September 21, 1897, and was reprinted for many years in the December 24 edition of that newspaper. It was also one of the very first stories that I read for "As It Happens" many years ago. Almost one hundred years after little Virginia O'Hanlon first wrote to the* New York Sun, *and then read the editor's response to her query in the pages of that paper, "Yes, Virginia, There is a Santa Claus" remains an endearing affirmation of a child's fancy, faith and vision.*

W e take pleasure in answering at once and thus promi-nently the communication below, expressing at the same time our great gratification that its faithful author is numbered among the friends of *The Sun*:

Dear Editor, I am 8 years old.

Some of my little friends say there is no Santa Claus.

Papa says "If you see it in The Sun it's so."

Please tell me the truth. Is there a Santa Claus?

Virginia O'Hanlon
115 West Ninety-fifth Street

VIRGINIA, Your little friends are wrong. They have been affected by the skepticism of a skeptical age. They do not believe
except they see. They think that nothing can be which is not
comprehensible by their little minds. All minds, Virginia,
whether they be men's or children's, are little. In this great uni-
verse of ours man is a mere insect, an ant, in his intellect, as
compared with the boundless world about him, as measured by
the intelligence capable of grasping the whole of truth and
knowledge.

Yes, Virginia, there is a Santa Claus. He exists as certainly as
love and generosity and devotion exist, and you know that they
abound and give to your life its highest beauty and joy. Alas!
how dreary would be the world if there were no Santa Claus! It
would be as dreary as if there were no Virginias. There would be
no childlike faith then, no poetry, no romance to make tolerable
this existence. We should have no enjoyment, except in sense
and sight. The eternal light with which childhood fills the world
would be extinguished.

Not believe in Santa Claus! You might as well not believe in
fairies! You might get your papa to hire men to watch in all the
chimneys on Christmas Eve to catch Santa Claus, but even if
they did not see Santa Claus coming down what would that
prove? Nobody sees Santa Claus but that is no sign that there is
no Santa Claus. The most real things in the world are those that
neither children nor men can see. Did you ever see fairies dancing on the lawn? Of course not, but that's no proof that they are
not there. Nobody can conceive or imagine all the wonders
there are unseen and unseeable in the world.

You tear apart the baby's rattle and see what makes the noise
inside, but there is a veil covering the unseen world which not
the strongest man, not even the united strength of all the
strongest men that ever lived, could tear apart. Only faith, fancy,
poetry, love, romance, can push aside that curtain and view and
picture the supernal beauty and glory beyond. Is it all real? Ah,
Virginia, in all this world there is nothing else real and abiding.

No Santa Claus! Thank God! he lives, and he lives forever. A
thousand years from now, Virginia, nay, ten times ten thousand
years from now, he will continue to make glad the heart of
childhood.

The
Gift of the Magi

by
O. HENRY
(1862–1910)

"And when they were come into the house, they saw the young child with Mary, his mother, and fell down, and worshipped him; and when they had opened their treasures, they presented unto him gifts: gold, and frankincense, and myrrh." In his story of "The Gift of the Magi," O. Henry plays most magically upon the old adage of value and value, worth and worth: the surface value of the gift; and what the gift is really worth. Della and Jim, as they find out, have between them something that cannot be valued: that which is valueless, and invaluable.

One dollar and eighty-seven cents. That was all. And sixty cents of it was in pennies. Pennies saved one and two at a time by bulldozing the grocer and the vegetable man and the butcher until one's cheeks burned with the silent imputation of parsimony that such close dealing implied. Three times Della counted it. One dollar and eighty-seven cents. And the next day would be Christmas.

There was clearly nothing to do but flop down on the shabby little couch and howl. So Della did it. Which instigates the moral reflection that life is made up of sobs, sniffles, and smiles, with sniffles predominating.

While the mistress of the home is gradually subsiding from the first stage to the second, take a look at the home. A furnished flat at $8 per week. It did not exactly beggar description, but it certainly had that word on the lookout for the mendicancy squad.

In the vestibule below was a letter-box into which no letter would go, and an electric button from which no mortal finger could coax a ring. Also appertaining thereunto was a card bearing the name "Mr. James Dillingham Young."

The "Dillingham" had been flung to the breeze during a former period of prosperity when its possessor was being paid $30 per week. Now, when the income was shrunk to $20, the letters of "Dillingham" looked blurred, as though they were thinking seriously of contracting to a modest and unassuming D. But whenever Mr. James Dillingham Young came home and reached his flat above he was called "Jim" and greatly hugged by Mrs. James Dillingham Young, already introduced to you as Della. Which is all very good.

Della finished her cry and attended to her cheeks with the powder rag. She stood by the window and looked out dully at a gray cat walking a gray fence in a gray backyard. Tomorrow would be Christmas Day, and she had only $1.87 with which to buy Jim a present. She had been saving every penny she could for months, with this result. Twenty dollars a week doesn't go far. Expenses had been greater than she had calculated. They always are. Only $1.87 to buy a present for Jim. Her Jim. Many a happy hour she had spent planning for something nice for him. Something fine and rare and sterling—something just a little bit near to being worthy of the honor of being owned by Jim.

There was a pier-glass between the windows of the room. Perhaps you have seen a pier-glass in an $8 flat. A very thin and very agile person may, by observing his reflection in a rapid sequence of longitudinal strips, obtain a fairly accurate conception of his looks. Della, being slender, had mastered the art.

Suddenly she whirled from the window and stood before the glass. Her eyes were shining brilliantly, but her face had lost its color within twenty seconds. Rapidly she pulled down her hair and let it fall to its full length.

Now, there were two possessions of the James Dillingham Youngs in which they both took a mighty pride. One was Jim's gold watch that had been his father's and his grandfather's. The other was Della's hair. Had the Queen of Sheba lived in the flat across the airshaft, Della would have let her hair hang out the window some day to dry just to depreciate Her Majesty's jewels and gifts. Had King Solomon been the janitor, with all his treasures piled up in the basement, Jim would have pulled out his watch every time he passed, just to see him pluck at his beard from envy.

So now Della's beautiful hair fell about her, rippling and shining like a cascade of brown waters. It reached below her knee and made itself almost a garment for her. And then she did it up again nervously and quickly. Once she faltered for a minute and stood still while a tear or two splashed on the worn red carpet.

On went her old brown jacket; on went her old brown hat. With a whirl of skirts and with the brilliant sparkle still in her eyes, she fluttered out the door and down the stairs to the street.

Where she stopped the sign read: "Mme. Sofronie. Hair Goods of All Kinds." One flight up Della ran, and collected herself, panting. Madame, large, too white, chilly, hardly looked the "Sofronie."

"Will you buy my hair?" asked Della.

"I buy hair," said Madame. "Take yer hat off and let's have a sight at the looks of it."

Down rippled the brown cascade.

"Twenty dollars," said Madame, lifting the mass with a practised hand.

"Give it to me quick," said Della.

Oh, and the next two hours tripped by on rosy wings. Forget the hashed metaphor. She was ransacking the stores for Jim's present.

She found it at last. It surely had been made for Jim and no one else. There was no other like it in any of the stores, and she had turned all of them inside out. It was a platinum fob chain simple and chaste in design, properly proclaiming its value by substance alone and not by meretricious ornamentation—as all good things should be. It was even worthy of The Watch. As soon as she saw it she knew that it must be Jim's. It was like him. Quietness and value—the description applied to both. Twenty-one dollars they took from her for it, and she hurried home with the 87 cents. With that chain on his watch Jim might be properly anxious about the time in any company. Grand as the watch was, he sometimes looked at it on the sly on account of the old leather strap that he used in place of a chain.

When Della reached home her intoxication gave way a little to prudence and reason. She got out her curling irons and lighted the gas and went to work repairing the ravages made by generosity added to love. Which is always a tremendous task, dear friends—a mammoth task.

Within forty minutes her head was covered with tiny, close-lying curls that made her look wonderfully like a truant schoolboy. She looked at her reflection in the mirror long, carefully, and critically.

"If Jim doesn't kill me," she said to herself, "before he takes a second look at me, he'll say I look like a Coney Island chorus girl. But what could I do—oh! what could I do with a dollar and eighty-seven cents?"

At 7 o'clock the coffee was made and the frying-pan was on the back of the stove hot and ready to cook the chops.

Jim was never late. Della doubled the fob chain in her hand and sat on the corner of the table near the door that he always entered. Then she heard his step on the stair away down on the first flight, and she turned white for just a moment. She had a habit of saying little silent prayers about the simplest everyday things, and now she whispered: "Please God, make him think I am still pretty."

The door opened and Jim stepped in and closed it. He looked thin and serious. Poor fellow, he was only twenty-two—and to be burdened with a family! He needed a new overcoat and he was without gloves.

Jim stopped inside the door, as immovable as a setter at the scent of quail. His eyes were fixed upon Della, and there was an expression in them that she could not read, and it terrified her. It was not anger, nor surprise, nor disapproval, nor horror, nor any of the sentiments that she had been prepared for. He simply stared at her fixedly with that peculiar expression on his face.

Della wriggled off the table and went for him.

"Jim, darling," she cried, "don't look at me that way. I had my hair cut off and sold it because I couldn't have lived through Christmas without giving you a present. It'll grow out again—you won't mind, will you? I just had to do it. My hair grows awfully fast. Say 'Merry Christmas!' Jim, and let's be happy. You don't know what a nice—what a beautiful, nice gift I've got for you."

"You've cut off your hair?" asked Jim, laboriously, as if he had not arrived at that patent fact yet even after the hardest mental labor.

"Cut it off and sold it," said Della. "Don't you like me just as well, anyhow? I'm me without my hair, ain't I?"

Jim looked about the room curiously.

"You say your hair is gone?" he said, with an air almost of idiocy.

"You needn't look for it," said Della. "It's sold, I tell you—sold and gone, too. It's Christmas Eve, boy. Be good to me, for it went for you. Maybe the hairs of my head were numbered," she went on with a sudden serious sweetness, "but nobody could ever count my love for you. Shall I put the chops on, Jim?"

Out of his trance Jim seemed quickly to wake. He enfolded his Della. For ten seconds let us regard with discreet scrutiny some inconsequential object in the other direction. Eight dollars a week or a million a year—what is the difference? A mathematician or a wit would give you the wrong answer. The magi brought valuable gifts, but that was not among them. This dark assertion will be illuminated later on.

Jim drew a package from his overcoat pocket and threw it upon the table.

"Don't make any mistake, Dell," he said, "about me. I don't think there's anything in the way of a haircut or a shave or a shampoo that could make me like my girl any less. But if you'll unwrap that package you may see why you had me going awhile at first."

White fingers and nimble tore at the string and paper. And then an ecstatic scream of joy; and then, alas! a quick feminine change to hysterical tears and wails, necessitating the immediate employment of all the comforting powers of the lord of the flat.

For there lay The Combs—the set of combs, side and back, that Della had worshipped for long in a Broadway window. Beautiful combs, pure tortoise shell, with jeweled rims—just the shade to wear in the beautiful vanished hair. They were expensive combs, she knew, and her heart had simply craved and yearned over them without the least hope of possession. And now, they were hers, but the tresses that should have adorned the coveted adornments were gone.

But she hugged them to her bosom, and at length she was able to look up with dim eyes and a smile and say: "My hair grows so fast, Jim!"

And then Della leaped up like a little singed cat and cried, "Oh, oh!"

Jim had not yet seen his beautiful present. She held it out to him eagerly upon her open palm. The dull precious metal seemed to flash with a reflection of her bright and ardent spirit.

"Isn't it a dandy, Jim? I hunted all over town to find it. You'll have to look at the time a hundred times a day now. Give me your watch. I want to see how it looks on it."

Instead of obeying, Jim tumbled down on the couch and put his hands under the back of his head and smiled.

"Dell," said he, "let's put our Christmas presents away and keep 'em awhile. They're too nice to use just at present. I sold the watch to get the money to buy your combs. And now suppose you put the chops on."

The magi, as you know, were wise men—wonderfully wise men—who brought gifts to the Babe in the manger. They invented the art of giving Christmas presents. Being wise, their gifts were no doubt wise ones, possibly bearing the privilege of exchange in case of duplication. And here I have lamely related to you the uneventful chronicle of two foolish children in a flat who most unwisely sacrificed for each other the greatest treasures of their house. But in a last word to the wise of these days let it be said that of all who have gifts these two were the wisest. Of all who give and receive gifts such as they are wisest. Everywhere they are wisest. They are the magi.

The
Oxen

THOMAS HARDY
(1840–1928)

Poor Thomas Hardy spent years and years brooding darkly, "hoping it might be so." I don't think that he ever came to a defi-nite conclusion—not so far as I know. "The Oxen" is one of his finest and most-loved poems: a fitting note to close on—not brooding darkly—but simply hoping it might be so...

The Oxen

CHRISTMAS EVE, and twelve of the clock.
    "Now they are all on their knees,"
An elder said as we sat in a flock
    By the embers in hearthside ease.

We pictured the meek mild creatures where
    They dwelt in their strawy pen,
Nor did it occur to one of us there
    To doubt they were kneeling then.

So fair a fancy few would weave
    In these years! Yet, I feel,
If someone said on Christmas Eve,
    "Come; see the oxen kneel

"In the lonely barton by yonder coomb
    Our childhood used to know,"
I should go with him in the gloom,
    Hoping it might be so.

COPYRIGHT ACKNOWLEDGMENTS

Margaret Atwood. "The Santa Claus Trap" © Margaret Atwood. Reprinted by permission of the author.

Michael Bond. "Paddington's Christmas" from *More About Paddington* by Michael Bond. Used by permission of The Agency (London) Ltd.

Warren Clements. "A Puzzling Christmas Gift" from *The Globe and Mail,* copyright © 1982 Warren Clements. Reprinted by permission of the author.

Alphonse Daudet. "The Three Low Masses" from *Letters From My Windmill* by Alphonse Daudet, translated by Frederick Davies (Penguin Classics, 1978) copyright © Frederick Davies, 1978.

Gillian Ferns. "Christmas" from *Affirmations* by John Ferns, 1989. Reprinted by permission of Borealis Press Limited.

Frederick Forsyth. "The Shepherd." Copyright © 1976 by Frederick Forsyth, reproduced by permission of Curtis Brown Group Ltd., London.

"Gritibaenz" by Carole-Anne McCarthy from *Canadian Children's Annual 1978.* Reprinted by permission of Potlatch Publications Limited.

Nikos Kazantzakis. "In Calabria" from *Report to Greco* by Nikos Kazantzakis, translated by P. A. Bien. Reprinted by permission of Faber and Faber Ltd.

W.O. Mitchell. "Brian's Skates" from *Who Has Seen the Wind* by W.O. Mitchell. Used by permission of the Canadian Publishers, McClelland & Stewart, Toronto.

"The Morton Thompson Turkey" from *The Berton Family Cookbook* by Pierre Berton. Reprinted by permission of Pierre Berton Enterprises Ltd.

Conor Cruise O'Brien. "Long Day's Journey into Prayer" by Conor Cruise O'Brien. Reprinted by permission of Greene & Heaton Limited.

"Réveillon Tourtière from *The Canadian Living Christmas Book*. Reprinted by permission of Madison Press Books for Canadian Living Magazine.

Lillian Eugenia Smith. "Christmas Kitchen Fifty Years Ago" reprinted from *Memory of a Large Christmas* by Lillian Smith, with the permission of W.W. Norton & Company, Inc. Copyright © 1961, 1962 by Lillian Smith.

Dylan Thomas. "A Child's Christmas in Wales" by Dylan Thomas. Reprinted by permission of J.M. Dent.

David Weale. "The True Meaning of Crumbfest" from *An Island Christmas Reader* by David Weale. Reprinted by permission of Leo J. Deveau and The Acorn Press.